'We have a great deal in common, Sarah. More than you're aware of, but I'll come to that. I've got to take a chance and you could be it.'

'A chance at what?' Sarah asked, wishing he wouldn't keep talking in riddles.

Ben nodded a couple of times in grave consideration. 'You're a real possibility, Sarah. In fact, I'm sure we could make it work. And I always get this feeling when I'm on to something good.'

Sarah's pulse gave a little leap of apprehension. 'What do you mean ... on to something good?' she asked suspiciously.

'Better than good,' said Ben, with rich satisfaction. 'Never felt more sure of anything.'

Which was no answer at all. He hitched himself forward with an air of eagerness.

'Sarah, I know this will come as a terrible shock to you, but I'm in a terrible dilemma and I reckon you're my best shot. What I want ... what I need ... is for you to marry me.'

Books you will enjoy
by EMMA DARCY

THE WRONG MIRROR

Karen ought to hate Hal Chissolm—he had, after all, deprived her beloved sister of everything that mattered in life. She hated him fiercely, but she could not escape him. And the question slowly arose—did she really want to?

THE UNPREDICTABLE MAN

Lyn's parents were horrified when she left home and they learned that her next-door neighbour would be Peter Kelso, that notorious womaniser. Nevertheless Lyn did move, and found Peter much nicer than she had expected. But was her mother right—and was he just amusing himself until he was tired of her?

THE ONE THAT GOT AWAY

'Strong and fast, courageous and powerful.' Jillian compared Taylor Marshall to the giant marlin, but when she set out to attract him, she soon began to wonder who was the angler ... and who the fish ...

STRIKE AT THE HEART

Sunny King was 'an ill-mannered, uncivilised notoriety-seeker', and Jackie wanted nothing more to do with him. So how did he manage to create such a disturbance in her easy-going life?

THE POSITIVE APPROACH

BY
EMMA DARCY

MILLS & BOON LIMITED
ETON HOUSE   18–24 PARADISE ROAD
RICHMOND   SURREY   TW9 1SR

*First published in Great Britain 1987
by Mills & Boon Limited*

© Emma Darcy 1987

*Australian copyright 1987
Philippine copyright 1987
This edition 1987*

ISBN 0 263 75789 7

*Set in Plantin 11 on 13 pt.
01-1087-39218*

*Computer typeset by SB Datagraphics,
Colchester, Essex*

*Printed and bound in Great Britain by
Collins, Glasgow*

For Karen,
who wants to know if it really works out.

CHAPTER ONE

TWELVE pairs of eyes bored into Sarah.

For the last ten minutes she had welcomed their focused attention, but the interest she had generated around the conference table with her proposal had now turned to irritation. She herself was appalled at the interruption. She could hardly believe it. To be asked to take a personal telephone call . . . and in the middle of her sales pitch! It was unbelievable. No one—not for any reason—interrupted a conference. They were sacrosanct.

The secretary's eyes were full of apologetic appeal. Her hands were fumbling together in agitation. She knew how bad the situation was, and she also knew that she would probably have to bear the brunt of the blame for such an unprecedented move. Her voice shook as she stood her ground and reinforced her message.

'Your fiancé said it was extremely urgent and important, Miss Woodley. He would not take no for an answer and was most emphatic that it couldn't wait.'

The poor girl was distraught and it was obvious that Julian had wrung this action out of her. What could be so urgent and important? Sarah wondered dazedly, then pulled her wits together. It was paramount that she make a quick decision. Everyone was looking at her ... waiting ... and every moment lost would be counted against her. Besides, she had no choice. If it really was urgent and important she had to go to Julian.

Sarah knew exactly how the secretary felt. Blood was pounding through her head as she forced herself to meet the eyes around the table. She could see the judgement in them. At twenty-eight she was the youngest departmental manager in the room, and that in itself was a ready-to-hand indictment for breaking a rule that the older managers had always respected.

'Please excuse me. I won't be long,' she said as steadily as she could, but even she could hear the tremulous note in her voice.

The chairman nodded. That was all. Nobody said a word. Conscious of the thick silence behind her, Sarah made as fast an exit as could be made with dignity. The secretary followed on her heels, babbling directions to the telephone holding the open line to Julian. Sarah snatched up the receiver, every nerve jangling with alarm as she spoke.

'What's the matter, Julian?'

'Sarah ...' It was a sigh of exasperation. 'What took you so long?'

Her inner tension drove a sharp edge to her voice. 'I'm not supposed to be here, Julian. I'm still in conference.'

He laughed. A totally uncaring laugh. A red haze spread through Sarah's brain. Only the most rigid self-discipline held it at bay. 'You said it was urgent and important, Julian,' she reminded him tightly.

He took an infuriating length of time getting to the point. Sarah listened with a weird sense of unreality. He had called her out of conference to ask if he'd left some documents in her apartment the previous night. He didn't need them right now. He simply wanted to feel reassured that they had not been misplaced elsewhere. The matter was not so urgent or important that it could not have waited. Another hour or two would have made no difference at all.

Sarah felt too sick to argue the point with him. He had probably set her career back years, just on a selfish whim. She gave him his reassurance in a dead, flat voice and hung up on him. She stared blankly at the secretary for a long, frozen moment. The girl's hands fluttered apologetically.

'He said he wouldn't let you work here any more if I didn't get you.'

The red haze gathered volcanic force, blotting out any compassion for the girl's dilemma. 'No more calls,' Sarah commanded harshly. 'Not for any reason. Now or in the future. I don't care what anyone says. No more calls.'

'Yes, Miss Woodley,' came the quivering reply.

But the damage was done. Sarah knew it as soon as she re-entered the conference room. No one looked at her except the chairman who informed her very briefly that they had considered her proposal for a new fashion line and decided that it carried too high a risk factor. Better to stick to proven lines where the profitability was certain.

Sarah flicked a look at Frances Chatfield, the manager of the Ladies' Fashion department. The triumph in the older woman's eyes told her that Frances had swung her entrenched influence against the proposal. Sarah had expected it. Frances Chatfield fiercely resented that Young Trends had been made into a separate department and given into the charge of a younger woman. Julian's call had delivered the perfect opportunity for her to suggest that Sarah's judgement was unreliable. The suggestion had taken root well and truly. Sarah could see it written all over their faces. In huge letters. UNRELIABLE.

Normally she fought for what she believed in. But to do that now with any chance of success she had to be calm and rational. The boiling rage inside her made such a state of mind impossible. If she spoke, she would only compound the damage. To all outward appearances she accepted defeat gracefully and was an attentive, respectful listener for the rest of the meeting.

The next seven hours were a different matter. She seethed over Julian's arrogant presumption that his needs had total priority over everything else. Never mind *her* career! Her job wasn't important enough for him to give it any serious consideration at all. He didn't care that his damned telephone call had undermined every bit of respect she had ever fought for.

Sarah prided herself on being tolerant. Dealing with customers in her Young Trends department made tolerance absolutely necessary, and the occasional necessity of dealing with Frances Chatfield demanded even more—tactful diplomacy and the patience of a saint. But by the time five o'clock came round, Sarah didn't feel at all tolerant. Her temper was sizzling on a very short fuse.

With a thoroughly jaundiced eye she scanned the oncoming stream of peak-hour traffic as she stood on the pavement outside the department store, waiting for Julian. When she spotted the red Alfa Romeo she moved to the kerb on a surge of angry impatience and ignored Julian's smile as he pulled in to pick her up. She slid quickly into the passenger seat and the short rein on her temper was frayed even further by his heavy-footed burst of acceleration. How many times had she told him she didn't like being jerked backwards while she was trying to fasten the seat-belt?

'It's great to have the week's work finished,' he tossed at her brightly. 'Did you have a good day?'

'No, thanks to you,' grated Sarah. 'And it may have escaped your notice, Julian, but my weekend doesn't start on Friday afternoon. I do have to work Saturday mornings as well.'

He frowned. 'We'll have to do something about that when we're married, Sarah. This working on Saturdays will interfere with our weekends together. Maybe you should start looking for a less demanding job.'

The last thread of control snapped. Sarah glared her fury and frustration at the man beside her. Neither the handsome profile nor the smart executive image that Julian affected so well made any softening impression on her. The words spilled off her tongue with all the steam of a pressure cooker whose lid had been lifted.

'Nothing can interfere with your plans, can it, Julian?' she stormed at him. 'In case it hasn't penetrated yet, let me tell you again. I *like* my job. I do not appreciate your cavalier attitude towards it. I particularly do not appreciate being pulled out of an important conference for an unnecessary telephone call. You know that such calls are completely against the company policy.'

He shot her a needled look. 'Now, hold on a minute, Sarah. That call was important. I was worried about those papers.'

'You could have waited an hour. You could have waited all day. If you had been the slightest bit thoughtful, you could have left a message for me to ring you back,' she retorted heatedly.

He laughed that same uncaring laugh. And then he patted her knee as he spoke with amused indulgence. 'Darling, it was in your own interests.

It was a way of showing those petty women you work with that when you're with me, their little power games don't matter. Now, what difference did it make?'

'They wouldn't listen to me, that's what difference it made, Julian,' she fired at him furiously. 'They'll probably never listen to my ideas again. And we're going to lose out on a contract with one of the most exciting young designers on the fashion scene, because Frances Chatfield hasn't got the eye to see it, and they no longer trust me to judge what's profitable or not.'

Julian shrugged. 'Well, why should you? You won't even need a job after we're married. I don't see what you're making so much fuss about,' he argued dismissively.

And he never would see, Sarah decided on a wave of disgust—disgust with his male chauvinist ego, and disgust at the way she had kept swallowing it all up until now. She hadn't minded Julian's arrogance at first. She had always admired ambitious, strong-minded men who knew where they were going and knew what they wanted out of life. But she did have a few ideas and plans of her own, and ever since she had accepted Julian's proposal of marriage, he had started to disregard them. From the moment she had said yes, it seemed that her feelings didn't count any more.

This wasn't the first argument they had had on the matter, but it was going to be the last, Sarah silently determined. She was not going to live the rest of her life with a man who always put himself first. If he treated his fiancée as a second-class citizen, how was he going to treat his wife? Particularly a wife who gave up all independence to have his children? Sarah was not so blinded by her emotional attachment to Julian that she couldn't see the kind of future that was staring her in the face, and she couldn't ignore it any longer.

'Oh, by the way, I ran into an old acquaintance today,' Julian remarked, completely unaware of her burning anger. He threw her a condescending smile. 'He's only in Sydney this weekend, so I promised I'd have lunch with him tomorrow. It'll make us a bit late leaving for your parents' place, but an hour or two won't matter.'

Sarah's anger gathered furnace heat. 'Funnily enough, it does matter, Julian.'

He sliced her a look that said she was being petty. 'If good humour is to be maintained, my sweet, the shorter the time we have with your parents, the better.'

'Let's make that no time at all,' she bit out decisively.

He sighed. 'Don't be unreasonable, Sarah. I'll put myself out to please your parents, but . . .'

'Don't bother. There's no reason for you to put yourself out for me or my parents. We're finished, Julian. This is the end.' She pulled off her ring and very deliberately placed it on the dashboard.

And finally he did take some notice of her. His smug composure broke into angry exasperation. 'For God's sake! Not another tantrum about your parents. You've said yourself that the only conversation they have is about gardening and lawn-bowls and bridge. It'll be a damned bore to me, but I'm willing ...'

'Forget it!' Sarah sliced in even more angrily. 'You're as free as a bird.'

'Don't be silly,' he said with a return to pompous arrogance.

'I'm not,' retorted Sarah emphatically.

He heaved a very patient sigh. 'You are being ridiculous. This is a foolish, self-defeating decision of yours, Sarah. It's not as if you're a young, skittish girl with lots of marriage prospects in front of you. The thing I've always appreciated about you is how sensible and reasonable you are ...'

Sarah seethed in stony silence, scorning any reply to his self-serving arguments. He pulled up at her apartment block in Neutral Bay with the usual abrupt braking that jerked her forward. She slammed out of the car. Julian followed her at a run. With absolute disdain for his heated expostulations, she marched straight into an open elevator and pressed the button for her floor. Julian accompanied her up, his face becoming quite red as she maintained her silence.

He grabbed her arm as she stepped out of the elevator, but Sarah tore it from his grasp and made a pointed business of getting her key out of her handbag. She noticed with an almost curious detachment that Julian's frustration was making him look quite ugly. The suave, man-about-town veneer was crumbling.

She unlocked her door and swept inside the apartment she shared with her friend, Angela Haviland. She hoped Angela was at home. Her presence would surely stem Julian's protests.

A rustle of newspaper drew her gaze to the couch. A big man lay stretched out on it, feet dangling over the end and head propped up on a cushion for easy reading. Sarah's step faltered for a moment. Who the devil was he? One of Angela's boyfriends? He had to be a new acquisition, because Sarah had never seen him before in her life.

She gave herself a quick mental shrug. Whoever he was he meant nothing to her. Her first priority was to get Julian off her back and out of her life. She swooped on the folder of notes that had been left on the coffee table last night and wheeled on Julian, who had spluttered into silence at the sight of the stranger.

'Here are your precious notes! They're more important to you than I am, so take them and go!' She thrust them into his hands.

There was a rustle of newspaper and Julian flicked a resentful glance at the man behind her. 'We have to talk about this, Sarah,' he said in a low, threatening tone.

'There's nothing more to say. I'm not cut out to suit your convenience, Julian. Go find yourself another doormat, because I'm not going to be one for you any more. I'd rather stay on the shelf by myself than live with you on your terms.'

'Now, Sarah ...' he tossed the folder on to the nearest armchair and took a firm hold of her upper arms, ' ... you can't change your mind like this. And when I say we'll talk, that means we're going to talk.'

'Let go of me, Julian,' she hissed, her inner rage boiling up again at his domineering tactics.

He ignored her, his gaze stabbing over her shoulder to the man on the couch. 'Would you mind leaving us alone? This is private.'

'Oh, no, you don't!' Sarah snapped, and out of sheer frustration that he wouldn't take notice of her, she drew back her foot and kicked him as hard as she could on the shin.

Julian flung her away with an angry oath. Thrown off balance, Sarah crashed back into the coffee table, stumbled over and felt herself falling backwards. She landed on the floor with a resounding thump along with the upturned table, a cup and saucer, and the frog ornament of which Angela was so fond. Her stunned gaze caught a blur of movement.

'Steady on, old chap. We can't be hitting women now, can we?'

The voice was modulated with sweet good

humour but, as Sarah's vision cleared, she saw that the stranger had Julian's wrist in a vice-like grip, and despite the tone of sweet reason, there was something definitely threatening about his stance next to her erstwhile fiancé. He was a very big man, taller and broader than Julian, and the track suit he wore fairly bulged with well developed muscles.

'Who are you?' demanded Julian, forced to take the stranger into consideration and furious with his interference.

The stranger ignored him, looking down at Sarah with a troubled frown. 'Are you hurt?' he asked, his voice softening to real concern.

'I ... I don't think so,' she said, testing her shaken limbs as she dragged herself into a sitting position.

'What do you want me to do with him—throw him out the window or the door?'

He could do it too, Sarah thought on a hysterical note of whimsy, and obviously Julian thought the same. 'I'll leave under my own steam,' he blustered, trying to pull his arm out of the stranger's grasp, but to no avail. He glared balefully at Sarah. 'It's obvious you've been two-timing me on the side. It's got nothing to do with your damned parents, has it?'

'I think the window. It's the least troublesome thing to do,' the big man said quietly, looking Julian straight in the eye.

'We're four storeys up,' gasped Sarah.

'A good dropping height,' he agreed. 'Gives him a nice view on the way down.'

Fear instantly shrivelled Julian's bravado. 'You're a maniac!' he squawked.

'Some very thick-headed people have called me that from time to time,' his captor conceded pleasantly.

'Let him go,' Sarah sighed, weary of the distasteful scene.

The big man leaned over, picked up the folder of the notes and presented it to Julian with a smile so benevolent that it spelled the most terrible danger. 'I'd go while the going was still easy if I were you,' he said softly.

Julian almost scuttled away, only pausing to square his shoulders into some dignity as he reached the door. 'You haven't heard the last of this!' he snarled at Sarah.

The big man moved fractionally. Julian did not stop to hurl any more invective. He swung on his heel and was off, slamming the door behind him.

Sarah dragged in a deep breath. She suddenly felt quite sick and very shaky. Before she could bring herself to move, the stranger was kneeling beside her, tenderly brushing away the long bang of hair that had flopped across her cheek.

'Are you all right?'

It was the soft, caring tone that did it. Throughout this whole terrible day, no one had cared how she felt. Tears welled into her eyes. 'I . . . I'm not sure,' she choked out.

'Hey . . .' his smile was softly admiring, 'you can't fall apart on me now. The way you told that guy where to get off was terrific. Greatest speech I've ever heard from a woman. Real backbone.' And so saying, he slid his arms under Sarah and, seemingly without any effort at all, cradled her against him like a helpless baby as he pulled himself to his feet.

But Sarah was a long way from being a baby. Although she was slim, she was above average height and her figure was very much that of a woman. No man had ever swept her up in his arms like this and it gave her a funny, weak feeling to be enveloped by so much virile strength.

She found her head disconcertingly close to his. Rather dazedly she looked into a pair of vivid blue eyes that were sparkling with pleasure at her. His smile was vivid too. Very white in his tanned face. And he had dimples in his cheeks. Dimples that looked hopelessly incongruous in what was a rugged kind of face; a firm, squarish jawline, a strong, slightly bent nose, a small, pale scar cutting through one of his straight eyebrows, and thick, bristly brown hair that was cut in a short, neat style.

'Who are you?' she finally croaked, suddenly feeling that it was time she grasped some control over the situation. 'And what are you doing in my apartment?' she added, realising belatedly that Angela had not put in an appearance to claim him.

One eyebrow rose in amusement. 'You took the words right out of my mouth.'

Sarah didn't understand him. 'What do you mean?'

He grinned. 'I was about to ask the same thing. Not that I object, mind you. You're very welcome. But I would like to know who you are, and what you're doing in my apartment.'

Sarah's head whirled. If she wasn't mad, then she was in the clutches of a crazy intruder. 'I think you'd better put me down,' she said warily.

He considered it for a moment and then shook his head. 'You're better off where you are,' he said in a very decided tone.

She had no hope of fighting him, not from this helpless position. She had seen him hold Julian with one hand. She swallowed hard and tried to keep calm. 'I don't know what game you're playing, but I'm Sarah Woodley. And my flatmate, Angela Haviland, will be home any minute now.' If he had any designs on her, the thought of witnesses suddenly appearing might slow him down.

'Sarah,' he said, then gave a deep chuckle of satisfaction. 'So you're Angela's flatmate! But that's marvellous! Absolutely perfect. Couldn't be better if I'd put in a custom-made order.'

'What couldn't be better?' she demanded testily.

'Just let me think for a minute,' he commanded, and without any regard for her dignity at all, he paced around the room, still carrying her effortlessly as though she were a rag doll he had momentarily forgotten.

His face was such a deep study of concentration that Sarah wasn't sure if it was wise to break his train of thought. She was in a perilous position and she didn't want him throwing her out of the window. But he had mentioned Angela's name. That was a consoling thought. Except that she had mentioned it first, so that particular consolation wasn't very dependable.

He came to an abrupt halt and the blue eyes were suddenly stabbing straight into hers with decisive purpose. 'You'll do, Sarah. Under the circumstances, I couldn't possibly do better. No doubt about it. All the other women I know will only give me trouble. Every one of them. Angela is out scouting for me now, but that's grasping at straws.'

'What are you talking about?' Sarah shrilled, desperate to find some grain of sense in what he was saying.

He smiled. Under normal conditions it was a smile that would have inspired confidence in him, and for a moment, Sarah was dazzled into being a compliant listener again.

'Sarah, I've been looking for someone like you. Desperately. And now that we've got rid of your fiancé . . . and from what I saw of him, I'd say good riddance . . . we'll spend the whole weekend together, getting to know each other. Make sure it's right,' he added with relish.

Her compliance took an immediate dive. 'I am not going to spend the weekend with you,' she cried in panicky protest. 'Angela ...'

' ... is my sister. I bought this apartment for her and that's one of the reasons she'll do anything for me. I'm Ben Haviland, her older brother. And I'm delighted to meet you, Sarah Woodley. In fact, I wish I'd come home a lot sooner. It would have taken some of the worry off my mind. Only got in from the States yesterday. Slept off the jet lag in the Hilton Airport Hotel and contacted Angela first thing this morning. Speed is of the essence and I hate staying in hotels anyway. Never feel comfortable in them.'

The panic receded. Angela had often talked of her 'maverick' brother, Ben. With admiration and exasperation. But all the same, Sarah still could not feel comfortable with the situation. 'Please ... I think you should put me down.'

The eyebrows slanted an appeal. 'It feels good, holding you like this. And it's making you feel better. Tears all gone. Voice stronger. Colour in your cheeks ...'

'Please ... I would like to sit down,' Sarah insisted, aware of an even greater rush of colour to her cheeks. 'And where is Angela?'

'As I said, she's out scouting prospects for me,' he said patiently. 'She said she'd call you at work and let you know what was going on.'

Sarah remembered her order about no calls and

heaved a sigh. 'She couldn't get through to me. Not today.'

'Then that answers everything.'

It answered nothing. However, to Sarah's relief he began to carry her towards the couch. His face beamed with the pleasure of someone who has just won a lottery.

'When will Angela be home?' she asked as he set her down on the seat cushions and released her.

'Probably not until Sunday night. She thinks there might be a couple of possibilities for me in Melbourne. How are your toes?'

To her startled surprise, he whipped off her shoes, lifted her feet on to the up-ended coffee table and was gently massaging the stockinged toes of her right foot before Sarah could voice a reply. 'Should have put the knee in, you know. Much more effective than a kick to the shins.'

'And you mean to stay here in the apartment with me?' she squeaked. His fingers were doing funny things to the toes and sole of her foot, making her feel quite squirmish.

'All weekend,' he agreed. As if he sensed her dismay he looked up in surprise. 'Well, it is my apartment. It cost me quite a lot of money, but I can't imagine anyone I'd rather share it with. I know this weekend is going to be great,' he said with a conviction that Sarah was far from feeling.

He wriggled her toes a few more times, gave her sole a couple of playful taps, then straightened up, eyeing her with sparkling anticipation. 'Now I'll get you a drink. Do you good. Prepare you for what's coming, because there's a lot of things you don't understand.'

You could say that again, Sarah thought with some asperity.

'How about a sherry?' he suggested brightly. 'I saw a bottle in one of the kitchen cupboards.'

'Thank you.' Sarah couldn't find voice for any other words. Ben Haviland was not only big, he was positively overwhelming. She certainly needed a drink to restore some equilibrium. It had been a very rocky day, and she wasn't at all sure that the weekend ahead wouldn't be even rockier.

CHAPTER TWO

'I CAN see you're a very positive person,' Ben declared, smiling approval at Sarah as he handed her a glass tumbler full of sherry.

Either he knew nothing about sherry or he thought she was an alcoholic, Sarah mused, eyeing the huge amount of amber liquid in the glass. There was probably a third of a bottle in it. 'This is a very large sherry,' she observed drily, as he settled into the armchair opposite her.

'Yes,' he agreed, and grinned.

Somehow the grin was infectious. A smile tugged at the corners of Sarah's mouth. 'I'm not that positive. Or negative. Whichever way you want to look at it. I only ever drink in moderation,' she added, in case he had any bright ideas about getting her drunk.

'That's good!' he said with even more approval. 'We have a great deal in common, Sarah. More than you're aware of, but I'll come to that. I've got to take a chance and you could be it.'

'A chance at what?' she asked, wishing he wouldn't keep talking in riddles.

He nodded a couple of times in grave consideration. 'You're a real possibility, Sarah. In fact, I'm sure we could make it work. The more I think about it, the more certain I feel. And I always get this feeling when I'm on to something good.'

Sarah's pulse gave a little leap of apprehension. 'What do you mean . . . on to something good?' she demanded suspiciously. He might be Angela's brother but the growing warmth of his regard was very discomfiting. And his gaze was roving over her in an openly assessing manner.

Sarah knew she looked good. It was part of her job to present a fashionable image and she worked at it. Her black hair was layered into a sleek shape that hugged the back of her head and sliced down to longer bangs that followed the curve of her cheeks. She knew all the tricks of make-up; how to emphasise her grey-green eyes, highlight her cheekbones, shade the roundness of her jawline. She had a long neck, and the height to wear any clothes well, and she had worn one of Penny Walker's brilliant new designs today, as an additional selling point to her sales pitch at the conference. The knitted fabric hugged her figure and the vibrant combination of black, green and violet was an eye-stopper.

'Better than good,' said Ben, with rich satisfaction. 'Never felt more sure of anything.'

Which was no answer at all. He hitched himself forward with an air of eagerness. Sarah took a defensive sip of sherry and then a larger one to loosen a sudden tension in her stomach. She refused to feel intimidated, but Ben Haviland certainly was a big strong man. The way he had held Julian so effortlessly was proof of that.

He was also disturbingly masculine. Aggressively masculine. Somehow he made her feel extremely conscious of being a woman. She couldn't help noticing how the stretch fabric of his grey track suit had to do a lot of stretching across the powerfully muscled thighs, and that the broad shoulders completely blotted out the backrest of the armchair. However, his smile was reassuring. It was nothing but genial.

'Sarah, I know this will come as a shock to you, but I'm in a terrible dilemma and I reckon you're my best shot. What I want ... what I need ... is for you to marry me.'

To say she was stunned would have been the understatement of the year. After a few totally blank moments, Sarah's brain moved into sluggish gear. Either she hadn't heard right or Ben Haviland was definitely off his rocker. She gulped down a very large swig of sherry. The warm tingle of alcohol helped to jolt her thought processes along. Maybe it was a joke.

'Sorry, but you just saw me retire from the marriage stakes,' she said flippantly. 'The last thing I want in my life at present is a man. You'll have to find yourself another candidate.'

'You're really against marriage?' he queried seriously.

Sarah didn't want to think about it. If she did stop to consider what she had just done to her relationship with Julian, she would probably break down and cry for a week. But she certainly wasn't going to show her emotional distress to a stranger. She shot Ben Haviland a derisive look. 'You heard me spell it out to Julian. After what I've been through with him, I'm damned sure that marriage is a prison I don't wish to enter. Not with him, and certainly not with you.'

His face relaxed into another bright smile. 'You're so right. That's exactly how I feel about marriage. A suffocating prison.'

Sarah eyed him warily. Was he some kind of a nutcase? First he proposed marriage and in the next breath he was against it! Caution was in order, Sarah decided. At the first opportunity she would make a break for it and head home to her parents' place in the Blue Mountains. Staying in this apartment for the weekend was clearly out of the question. On Monday she would find out from Angela if her brother had ever been in a psychiatric institution. Meanwhile the sensible thing to do was humour him.

'Why are you against marriage?' she asked solemnly.

He winced and shook his head. 'I had the most dreadful experience. Worse than yours. I was almost at the altar when I finally realised how badly I'd been deceived. The woman I was going to marry had actually lined up a job for me and wanted me to take it. Can you imagine that? Thinking she could push me into work!'

He shuddered at the thought. 'And that was only the last straw. I won't bore you with the rest. I tell you, Sarah, there was only one thing to do. I ran. You might think that was cowardly, but if you knew the woman you'd understand. She wanted everything her way and me under her thumb. Couldn't even see my point of view.'

Like Julian, Sarah thought bitterly, although the position was somewhat reversed. It was Julian's dismissal of her job that had been the last straw, not a demand that she take one. Yet if Ben Haviland didn't work, how had he got the money to buy this apartment for Angela?

Again she eyed him warily. There was no doubt that he was eccentric, but he didn't look mad. His claim about owning this apartment could be right. The rent was almost ridiculously low. Sarah had always thought how terribly lucky she had been in answering Angela's advertisement for a flatmate. Such a well appointed apartment with harbour views could easily command double the amount she paid Angela each week.

Curiosity drove Sarah to pick her words carefully, not wanting to offend the big man. 'If you don't work, Ben, how did you raise the capital to buy this apartment?'

'Used my brains,' he answered promptly. Then seeing her incomprehension, he added, 'What I do is sell ideas. Perfectly natural for a guy who hates work as I do. As it happens, I'm fairly good at coming up with things that have appeal for the general public. Too good this time, which is why I've got the problem I have.'

His mouth turned down into a grimace. 'I've had the best lawyers and accountants in the country working on it and they all come up with the same answer. Get married. Split your income with your wife. There's really no viable alternative. I've got to do it, no matter what I feel. And time's running out. Today is the twentieth of May, and there are only forty-one days left. I must be married by the thirtieth of June.'

Sarah was completely lost in this line of logic, if indeed there was any line of logic. 'Why?' she asked, hoping to get a glimmer of light.

'Because it's the end of the financial year. If I'm not married by then, they're going to hit me hard, Sarah,' he said, shooting her a look of desperate appeal.

Sarah shook her head in bewilderment. 'Who's going to hit you hard?'

'The taxation department!' he spat out in disgust. 'It's a case of blatant discrimination. A married man can have a partnership and split his income, but an unmarried man has to bear double the burden. I don't mind paying my fair share. I do that anyway. I reckon I'm supporting half the welfare state as it is. But this is an absolute rip-off, Sarah, and the only way around it is to get married.'

Light dawned. Sarah heaved a sigh of relief. Ben Haviland wasn't mad at all. There was nothing mad about trying to hold on to a fair share of one's hard-earned cash. She offered him a sympathetic smile. 'Well, I'm sorry about your financial problems, but you can't really expect me to bail you out of them. It seems to me that marriage is a pretty drastic answer, particularly since you see it as a trap. Better to pay up and keep your freedom.'

He held up a hand and put on a grave face. 'You don't understand. Truly you don't. It's big money. Really big. All my chickens have come home to roost at the same time. I'm in desperate trouble. In the normal course of events I wouldn't think of proposing.'

The grave face slowly melted into a pleased grin as he relaxed back into the chair. His eyes sparkled absolute delight at her. 'But you and I, Sarah— that's something else again. We'd make the ideal partnership,' he said with relish.

Her heart gave a funny little lurch. She took several gulps of sherry to steady an oddly wayward pulse. There was a smug air of confidence about him that she wanted to prick. He had no right to be looking at her like that. It was presumptuous, and, God knew, she'd had enough of presumptuous men. After her experience with Julian, she doubted that she would ever trust another man in any relationship. Men didn't want to be partners with women. Not equal partners.

She fixed Ben Haviland with a sceptical eye. 'The last thing I need is another man to screw up my life. I've already been through that. The moment you let a man in your life, he starts making demands, and the longer the relationship goes on, the more demanding he becomes.'

'Same with a woman,' Ben said with feeling. 'They never know when to stop. Why can't they let a man be himself? Always trying to change him!'

His counter-claim stirred the boiling well of resentment that was still simmering inside her. 'Huh!' she responded scornfully. 'You don't even see the other side of the coin. Let me tell you what Julian did to me today . . .' And she spilled out the whole chain of events, reliving it again with vehement passion.

It was good to let it all out, and Ben Haviland was the perfect listener. He muttered sympathetic comments. His expressions mirrored her own feelings, apparently in absolute accord with the sentiments she was expressing. When she finally wound down he shook his head over the whole affair in appreciative understanding for all that she had suffered, and sat in sympathetic silence while they both contemplated the mean crimes some people perpetrated on others.

'You should have let me drop him out of the window,' Ben said finally. 'The whole trouble is, neither men nor women show their true colours until they think they've got you tied up.'

'Exactly,' Sarah sighed, and took another sip of sherry. Her throat was quite dry from all the talking she had done.

Ben Haviland was right, she decided. They did have a lot in common, and it was nice to have someone on a sympathetic wavelength with her, particularly after the terribly stressful day she had been through. She looked across at him and smiled, grateful for his company, however eccentric he was. He obviously took her smile as an encouraging signal for he began to argue his cause again.

'We wouldn't be like that, Sarah,' he said with firm conviction. 'Don't you see how ideal it is? Both of us want to live life on our own terms, and we can do it if we get together. It's the perfect arrangement. You'll have the financial security of being married to me and the Government can't bleed me white. It'll save us a lot of money, Sarah.

A lot of money. And don't think I won't be appreciative.'

Promises, promises, Sarah thought with all the bitterness of her recent disillusionment. While she now understood Ben's dilemma, she certainly didn't feel she wanted to be the answer to it. 'You're the one who has to get married. Not me,' she pointed out decisively. 'And I'm quite capable of supporting myself, thank you.'

She lifted her glass in a mocking toast to him and swallowed some more sherry, then realised she was beginning to feel a bit fuzzy in the head. She frowned down at the glass in her hand and saw that it was three parts empty. She had inadvertently drunk far more than she had intended. Annoyed with herself, she leaned over and placed the tumbler on the coffee table with a decisive bang.

Ben caught hold of her hand as she withdrew it from the glass. He had hitched himself forward again, and when she looked up, his face was quite close to hers and the blue eyes held a mesmerising intensity of purpose.

'Sarah . . . how would you like to run your own boutique? Complete authority. Buy and sell whatever you like. Do whatever you want, whenever you want.'

It was her favourite daydream, although she knew it would never be possible because there was no way she could ever raise enough capital. Every week she took tickets in LOTTO in the faint hope that maybe one day she might get lucky and win the big first prize. That was her only chance of ever getting enough money to do what she wanted. One thing she did trust, however, was her instinct for what fashions would sell well, and she had no doubt that she could run a successful boutique.

'Sarah, I can give you the financial backing you need to run the best fashion boutique in Sydney. You can have a completely free hand to set up whatever you want. Everything you need. Cost no object. But I need a wife.'

She looked blankly at Ben, not quite taking in what he was offering. He bounced to his feet, and pulled her to hers as he swiftly rounded the coffee table. He let go her hand and gently cupped her face, forcing her attention.

'Any location you like. Double Bay, inner city . . . whatever fashion goods you want to sell. All you have to do is marry me before the thirtieth of June. A favour for a favour, Sarah. That's fair, isn't it?'

'You . . . you can't mean it,' she stammered disbelievingly.

'There's that much money involved in it, Sarah. Word of honour. Better still, I'll get my solicitor to write up a marriage contract setting out the terms. How's that?'

'But . . . I . . . I can't marry you just to . . . to . . .'

'Of course you can.' His hands dropped from her

face to slide around her waist and draw her closer to him. 'You're a free agent now. You can do anything you want. Jut think of it, Sarah. You can do your own thing with absolute authority. No money problems. No one dictating how you're to run your life. Our marriage wouldn't be a prison, Sarah.'

The future he was painting danced before her eyes, compellingly attractive, a fantasy of limitless possibilities. She stared up at him and felt caught in the excitement that lit his face.

'And there's nothing about you I'd want to change, Sarah,' he said emphatically. 'I think you're perfect, just as you are.'

And while Sarah was still trying to work some sanity into her befuddled mind, Ben translated his appreciation into more physical terms, his mouth descending on hers with a kiss that was startlingly persuasive in its sheer sensuality. Sarah hadn't meant to respond. In fact, one corner of her mind told her she should be properly outraged by the liberties he was taking with her person. It wasn't just the kiss. His embrace was drawing her closer and closer to him, making her terribly aware of the hard masculinity of his body. And his hands were caressing the curve of her spine with a gentle, knowing pressure that was both comforting and pleasurable.

Sarah made a valiant effort to focus her mind. This had to be stopped. This morning she had been engaged to Julian, and no matter how disaffected she was with him, to be accepting and responding to another man's kiss . . . and body . . . it just wasn't right. It had to be all that sherry . . . making her light-headed . . . or something. Reluctantly but determinedly she dragged her mouth away from his and turned her head aside, sucking in a deep, steadying breath before attempting to break the embrace.

Ben gave her little breathing space. His mouth moved to her ear and awakened a sensitivity that tingled through her whole body. 'Don't!' she gasped.

'Can't help it. It's your perfume drawing me on,' he murmured, caressing the long line of her throat with nibbling little kisses that totally seduced the protest on Sarah's tongue.

'*Impulse*,' she breathed, as if that explained everything.

'Very strong,' Ben agreed huskily, one hand roaming closer to the underswell of her breast.

'No. The perfume. It's called *Impulse*,' Sarah said on a shivery sigh. The hand had found an erotic line just under her armpit and really it was quite terrible how weakly receptive she was to its touch.

'Never felt more that way,' Ben murmured, moving her lower body to fit more intimately to his.

And that jolted Sarah back down to earth. Ben's

impulses were all too noticeably aroused. Shame shot through her like a bolt of lightning and jerked her out of his embrace. 'Stop!' she cried, in terrible agitation.

And he did stop. Abruptly. He pulled away and his face was a picture of hurt puzzlement at her vehement rejection.

'I'm sorry,' Sarah said limply. 'I shouldn't have let you do that. I don't know what got into me,' she babbled on, appalled at her uncharacteristic lapse of control.

'My fault,' Ben said in instant mitigation. 'I don't usually get carried away like that. Must have been a release of tension.'

'Yes,' she agreed quickly. It certainly had been a tense day.

'Fresh air. That's what we need. And a good solid meal. That'll clear our heads for serious planning. Let's go for a stroll and find a restaurant.'

Sarah couldn't get her shoes on fast enough. She didn't even consider what serious planning Ben had in mind. She just wanted to escape from the disturbing intimacy that had been generated in this apartment. He held the door open for her and she slipped past him quickly, far too physically aware of him even to meet his eyes.

'Angela said there's quite a good restaurant only a couple of blocks away,' Ben remarked as they rode down in the elevator.

'Yes,' said Sarah, choked by his nearness. The compartment seemed terribly small with Ben Haviland in it. She shook her head, trying to shake off the strange influence that he was having on her. She had never felt anything like it before in her whole life. 'Being with you is like riding on a roller-coaster,' she said ruefully.

He smiled a heart-catching smile. 'There's no one I'd rather ride with.'

Sarah felt hopelessly confused by her unwarranted reaction to him. 'You're going too fast,' she protested, almost panicking at the strange magnetism that was pulling her along with him.

'Time is the enemy,' he declared blithely, and caught her hand as they walked out of the apartment block.

She shot him an apprehensive glance, wondering if she was being incredibly foolish to accompany him anywhere when she was obviously not her usual sensible self. 'I haven't said I'll marry you,' she reminded him, but she left her hand in his. There was something rather nice about the way he held it. Firm, yet somehow caring. She liked it. It was friendly.

They walked one block in silence.

'I wouldn't make demands on you, Sarah,' Ben said seriously. 'If we're not in mutual agreement about something, then you go your way and I'll go mine. No argument. No pressures. OK?'

'OK,' she echoed, then berated herself for the unthinking agreement.

How could she marry a man she hardly knew? The idea was preposterous. On the other hand, what kind of future did she have to look forward to? Another thirty years in the department store, having her ideas stultified by people like Frances Chatfield? If she had her own boutique ... and, after all, it was really a business partnership she would have with Ben. Nothing personal.

The hand holding hers instantly mocked that last idea. And what had already happened between them mocked it even more. 'This marriage you want ... you aren't actually considering us living together, are you?' she asked, staring straight ahead as she felt a flush of embarrassment creeping up her neck. 'That's a hypothetical question, of course,' she added firmly.

'Well ... er ... very tricky things, hypothetical questions.' He paused a long time before answering her. 'Actually, I think that depends very much on the two people concerned, although living together is the usual situation when one gets married,' he finished matter-of-factly.

Sarah took a deep breath. 'I meant ... would you ... would you expect to go to bed with me?'

Again there was a long pause before he spoke, and when he did, it was even more hesitantly. 'Well—er ... what ... er ...' He took a deep breath.

'Umm . . . were you planning on being celibate for the rest of your life, Sarah?'

Which was a very tricky question. 'I'd have to think about it,' she muttered.

'Ah,' he said, and fell silent for another half a block. His fingers fondled hers as if he was in deep thought. Sarah couldn't bring herself to look at him. It really was terribly shameless the way she had responded to him. He probably thought she was promiscuous, which wasn't the case at all.

Ben suddenly stopped dead and turned to her with an air of decision. 'I won't lie to you. I certainly want to go to bed with you, Sarah. Can't deny it. In fact I can't remember when I ever felt so attracted to a woman. But that doesn't mean you have to go to bed with me. I'll respect your wishes. Any time you don't want to go to bed with me, all you have to do is say so. Fair enough?'

'Yes,' she said quickly, feeling a bewildering wave of relief. Was she relieved because he wanted her to share his bed . . . or because she didn't have to? Sarah shook her head over the idea as they resumed walking. She wasn't a sex-orientated person. Although she had found Julian's lovemaking quite pleasurable, at times, she had never initiated it. Nor had she craved for it. In fact, she didn't think she would even miss it.

But the rest of her life was a different matter, she argued to herself. She mightn't want to stay

celibate, and if she accepted Ben's proposal ...
which she wouldn't! It was crazy even to consider
it. She sneaked a quick sideways glance at him. In a
purely physical sense he was a very attractive man.
Big, but very well proportioned. If he was her
husband, she didn't think she'd mind going to bed
with him. The way he had kissed her ... he was
surely very, very good at making love.

'How old are you?' she blurted out.

'Thirty-four,' he answered promptly. 'And
you?'

'Twenty-eight.'

'That's good!' he said in some relief. 'Actually
you look younger. It worried me a bit.'

'Why?'

'I wouldn't like to think I was taking advantage
of a young girl on the rebound, so to speak. But you
impressed me as a woman who knows her own
mind, Sarah. And speaks it. You're a very positive
person. I like that. I like that very much.'

And his hand squeezed hers. Rather possessively,
Sarah thought, but found she didn't mind.

They reached the restaurant and were lucky
enough to find a table free. Ben ordered a bottle of
champagne with their meal.

'I really can't marry you,' Sarah insisted when
the waiter had departed.

His smile was slow and very warm. 'I feel like

champagne. Tell me all about yourself and your family.'

With the change of subject Sarah relaxed. 'I have three older brothers, all married with families. I'm the only girl and a terrible disappointment to my mother. She wants to see me married like the others.'

The thought brought an abrupt stab of guilt. 'Poor Mum! She's going to be upset with me, breaking my engagement with Julian. She and Dad were looking forward to meeting him. We were supposed to go up to Mount Victoria tomorrow afternoon and stay the weekend with them.' Her smile was full of bitter irony. 'For a discussion of wedding plans. But now . . .' Her hands fluttered in a gesture of hopelessness.

'Won't I do instead?' Ben asked.

She was startled by the offer. 'But—but you wouldn't want a proper wedding and—and all that goes with it!'

'Who said that? I don't mind. As long as we get married, I don't care how we do it. Might as well make your parents happy.'

'What about your parents?'

He shrugged. 'They gave up on me years ago. Nothing I do will surprise them. Apart from which they're overseas and won't be back for months.'

The bottle of champagne arrived along with their first course. Sarah was glad of something to eat. She was feeling distinctly light-headed. She wondered if she was mad enough to contemplate marriage with Ben Haviland, then decided that mad or not, she *would* contemplate it.

A smile tugged at her mouth. Everyone would think it a very odd marriage, but it was really nobody's business but hers and Ben's. And if Ben was willing to humour her parents, well, it was more than Julian had been willing to do. She wondered how Angela would react, and the thought prompted the question.

'What does Angela think about this marriage scheme?'

A surprisingly sheepish look flitted over Ben Haviland's face. 'She's ... umm ... working on it for me. I didn't know I was going to meet you, Sarah,' he added quickly.

The absurdity of the situation suddenly hit Sarah. She began to laugh, and when the laughter finally rippled down to a grin, she asked, 'How old were you when you almost made it to the altar the first time?'

'Twenty-four. And you can laugh, Sarah Woodley, but I can tell you it was deadly serious. Put me off the idea of marriage altogether. That woman was going to swallow me whole and chew me into little pieces,' he declared feelingly.

Sarah began to giggle again. 'She'd have to have a big mouth.'

'About as big as Julian's, I'd say,' he shot at her testily.

Sarah immediately sobered. He was right. If she had gone along with Julian, he would have swallowed her whole and chewed her into little pieces. 'I'm sorry,' she sighed as depression nibbled at her again.

'No, *I'm* sorry,' Ben said softly, and she looked up into kind, compassionate eyes. 'I've just remembered how bad I felt at the time. I guess you feel pretty bad, too. I wish I didn't have to rush you, Sarah, but I really haven't got any alternative.'

He was nice. A bit wacky, but nice. She smiled. 'Well, at least you've been very successful at distracting me from more miserable thoughts.'

'And you'll marry me?' he pressed eagerly.

For a moment Sarah thought—why the hell not? What did she have to lose? Any marriage was a gamble and this one would at least let her be herself. Ben was handing her the opportunity of a lifetime as far as a work situation was concerned. She would be a fool to turn it down. But could she live with the decision? It seemed so mercenary and cold-blooded.

'I'll think about it.'

'Please?'

The intense appeal in his eyes seemed very personal, not cold-blooded or mercenary at all. It muddled up her reasoning and she found herself thinking that she had lived very amicably with Angela for two years. And Ben was Angela's brother. Not that that meant anything, but ... maybe it could work very well. She imagined him always sitting across from her at the table. Her husband. He was certainly very attractive.

'It's a temptation,' she said slowly.

Happy relief spread across his face. 'That's great! Now we're getting somewhere. I knew you were a positive person, Sarah.'

'I haven't given you a positive answer,' she pointed out.

'Not yet,' he agreed, but his smile looked very confident as he filled her glass with champagne.

CHAPTER THREE

WAS she really taking Ben Haviland's proposal seriously, Sarah mused several times throughout the meal, or was it simply a pipe-dream that was far easier to contemplate than the inevitable consequences of today's events? She felt light-headed and heavy-hearted at the same time—probably the effect of all the sherry and champagne.

She watched, a little pie-eyed as Ben topped up her glass again. Some persistent threads of common sense told her she shouldn't drink any more, but she couldn't be bothered to voice a protest. What did it matter? What did anything matter?

Ben Haviland had nice eyes. They were like Angela's, open and honest, and she liked the way he was looking at her, as if she were a real prize, someone worth having. It proved that Julian was wrong with his arrogant claim that he was probably her last chance at marriage. Ben would have her tonight if she said yes. He found her desirable enough to go along with whatever she wanted.

But she didn't love him. She didn't love him and he didn't love her, and even though he was laying at her feet a bridge to a new kind of life, she would

48

be a fool to rely on it. She had been a fool to rely on Julian. It should be Julian sitting opposite her now, giving her the support that Ben was giving. Instead of that, Julian had uncaringly activated her defeat by that bitch, Frances Chatfield. Julian, who had said he loved her . . .

'Sarah, are you all right?'

The caring note in Ben's voice tripped her heart. The tears that had welled into her eyes made his face a blur but she could see he was leaning towards her in a pose of concern. She shook her head and blinked hard but the tears kept coming.

'It's been a hell of a day,' she confessed miserably.

'I'll get the bill. Take you home,' he said, quickly reacting to her need, his voice soft and his hand reaching across the table to press hers sympathetically.

He was as good as his word. Their waiter was immediately summoned, the bill disposed of in moments, and Ben was on his feet, helping Sarah to hers. His arm curled around her shoulders and it was comforting to lean her weight on him as he steered her to the exit. Once outside both of his arms came around her and Sarah was gently turned to face him.

'Why are you crying?'

'I'm not,' she denied, but she could not meet his eyes.

He lightly pressed her head on to his shoulder and his cheek rubbed over her hair. Sarah felt too worn out to resist and there was no threat in Ben's embrace. The warm strength of him enveloped her, supported her, made her feel cherished, and she desperately needed some cherishing.

'It's all right, Sarah,' he whispered. 'I won't let anyone hurt you. Ever again.'

The temptation to give up, to surrender herself into his keeping, was almost overwhelming in that moment of weakness. It felt right. Better to marry him than a lot of others. Possibly anyone. He would do more for her than most, and he didn't expect her to pamper his ego. Maybe love was only an illusion anyway. An understanding partnership was probably a more sensible foundation on which to build a purposeful future.

Ben hailed a passing taxi and bundled her into the back seat with him. 'We can walk. It's only a few blocks,' Sarah expostulated.

'You're dead on your feet. I'm taking you home the quickest way possible,' Ben replied, and gave the address to the cab driver.

The taxi pulled up outside the apartment block in a matter of moments and it seemed perfectly natural to lean on Ben as he helped her out. He hugged her close to him during the elevator ride up to the fourth floor and only let her go to usher her into the apartment after he had unlocked the door.

'Ben! Is that you?' Angela came charging out of the kitchen, her face alight with triumph. The change of expression was almost comic as she goggled at the pair of them, Sarah's head drooping against Ben's shoulder and his arm almost encircling her waist. 'What are you two doing together?' she demanded in startled surprise.

Sarah simply stared, her befuddled head only slowly coming to grips with Angela's unexpected appearance on the scene. It was Ben who voiced her thought.

'What are you doing back here? You're supposed to be in Melbourne,' he said on a critical note.

'Mission accomplished,' Angela retorted, eyeing her brother with some exasperation. 'And the least I expected of you was to remain where I could find you.'

Ben shrugged off the criticism. 'Just took Sarah out for a meal.'

Angela frowned at Sarah. 'I thought you'd be out with Julian.' The frown cleared as she added, 'But I'm glad you don't find my brother too objectionable. I was . . .'

'That's enough of that, Angela,' Ben cut in irritably.

She heaved a sigh and shook her head at her big brother as if he were a recalcitrant child. 'Just don't come to me for sympathy when this mad scheme of yours brings you grief.'

'It's not mad. Some of the best brains in the country advised me ...'

'I know. I know. But only you would try to get around it this way. Any normal person ...'

'Look who's calling the kettle black! If you were a normal woman, you wouldn't be a crime reporter.'

'I like reporting crime,' Angela said indignantly. 'And I like ...'

Sarah drifted to the nearest armchair and sat down. Her head felt dizzy. Angela and Ben were too involved in their argument to notice that she had removed herself from the field of battle. She watched them rave on at each other, noting there was no real animosity in their manner or speech. It was the kind of spat a brother and sister can enjoy with each other, familiarity and affection ensuring that there were no hard feelings left on either side.

Apart from their eyes, they shared little similarity in appearance. Angela was barely average height and rather petite in figure. Her hair might have been the same brown colour as Ben's but she regularly had blonde streaks put through it. This was to add more individuality to what she called her ordinary looks. She was pretty without being striking, and her pet hatred was other people observing that she reminded them of someone else.

She was not the least bit daunted by her brother's size, and a smile tugged at Sarah's mouth as Angela adopted her belligerent pose: hands on hips, chin lifted, eyebrows arched in scornful challenge. 'At least I know where I'm heading,' she declared loftily.

'And so do I!' Ben retorted with vehement authority.

'Huh!' scoffed Angela and put on a cynical smile. 'Then you should be grateful to me, Ben. I've found someone who will go through this charade of a marriage with you.'

That jolted Sarah out of her passive daze. It also pulled Ben up short. He shot an axious look at her then frowned heavily at his sister.

'Er ... matter of fact, Angela, I've found the woman I want myself. Not that I'm ungrateful for what you've done, but ...'

'Oh, that's great, that is!' Angela sniped at him. 'Now I'm left looking an absolute fool. As if it wasn't bad enough that I had to play the part of a shifty marriage agent ...'

The burst of indignation floated over Sarah's head. One word was echoing through her mind with devastating force ... charade ... a charade of a marriage ... and, of course, that was what it would be. No love, no substance to it, a pretence, just as Ben's caring for her tonight had probably been a pretence to get what he wanted. Suddenly the depression that his diverting company had kept at bay, descended on her with a vengeance. She rose stiffly to her feet and pasted a brittle smile on her face.

'Well, you won't be needing me any more, Ben. I'm sure Angela's candidate will fit the bill. If you'll both excuse me, I'd like to retire.'

Ben's hand flew out to detain her, his face a study in sincere appeal. 'Hold on, Sarah. I don't want to marry anyone else. No one could be better than you.'

'Sarah?' Angela's voice was an incredulous squawk. 'Now I know you're out of your mind, Ben. Sarah's already engaged to be married and she'd never——'

'We got rid of him,' Ben threw at her impatiently. 'Sarah and I are in total agreement about marriage. It's a fool's game and we're smart enough to——'

'What do you mean, you got rid of him?' Angela's mouth dropped open in horror as she turned to Sarah. 'My God! He hasn't messed things up with Julian, has he? I'll never forgive myself for leaving him here. I thought I could trust Ben to behave himself for once.'

'Dammit, Angela! I *did* behave myself,' Ben exploded in exasperation. 'I didn't throw him out of the window. I didn't even kick him out of the door. I let him go peaceably, just as Sarah said.'

'Oh, God!' Angela turned frantic eyes of apology

back to Sarah. 'I'll do whatever I can to fix it. I'm so sorry. So——'

Sarah stepped out of Ben's light grasp and gave her friend's arm a reassuring squeeze. 'It's all right, Angela. I called it off with Julian and he didn't take it well. I'm grateful to Ben for stepping in when he did. It saved me a nasty scene.'

Angela searched her eyes worriedly. 'You called it off, Sarah? But you've been crazy about him.'

Sarah heaved a sadly ironic sigh. 'Crazy stupid, I guess. Anyhow, it's over.'

'But why?' Angela shook her head, mystified, then in a burst of anxious concern, 'Well, whatever happened, you can't be crazy enough to take Ben on, Sarah! That's not what you want.'

'Hey! Whose side are you on, Angela?' Ben protested loudly.

'No, it's not what I want,' Sarah agreed dully. The tears gathered again and she blundered off down the hallway to her bedroom, needing quite desperately to nurse her heartache in private.

'Sarah!' Ben called after her.

'You leave her alone, you ... you numskull!' Angela berated him.

'You don't understand ...'

'If you think for one minute that Sarah's the type to—to sell herself to you, you're a bigger fool than I thought you were!'

'You've got it all wrong. We'd be partners, not——'

Sarah closed her door on the argument. Angela didn't have it wrong, she thought, sickened by the stark truth of the bargain she had almost made with Ben. He would have been buying her. She had even gone so far as to think of sharing her bed with him. Shame added its sting to her tears. She dragged off her clothes and climbed into bed, welcoming the darkness and the soft muffling of her pillow in which to bury her misery.

She didn't want the empty charade of a marriage that Ben offered. She wanted what Julian had promised, the sharing of their lives within the bond of love. She could tell herself she had been stupid and blind to ignore the way their relationship had been heading. She could tell herself she had been right to end it, but the hurt could not be dismissed quite so easily. A whole year of emotional involvement would not be cut dead. Julian had answered a lot of needs in Sarah that would not suddenly go away.

There were many pleasures they had enjoyed sharing: a love of dancing, skiing, dining out with friends. She had been proud of the way he could handle any social situation. He had been proud of her flair for fashion. They had looked good together and there had been a lot of social advantages in being an established couple. All gone now, Sarah mourned, and wondered if she had been a fool to throw it all away.

Maybe Julian had been right, and her job didn't matter. Was it her ego at fault, too wrapped up in a career position it had taken ten years to achieve? But it wasn't only Julian's arrogant lack of consideration over that, Sarah reminded herself. It was an ingrained attitude on his part, that had been chafing her for some time. Everthing would be fine as long as she went along with what Julian wanted. But how long could she have gone on swallowing her resentment at his cavalier dismissal of her wishes for the sake of peace between them? For a lifetime?

And it had been getting worse—Julian taking her submission to his selfish will more and more for granted. And he couldn't, or wouldn't even see that he was wrong. That was what made her so mad, so frustrated and . . . No, she couldn't have lived with it. Not in the long run. That wasn't her idea of love or of how a relationship should work between people who respected each other. It was too one-sided. Suffocatingly one-sided.

The tap on her door jerked Sarah's head up from the pillow, but the quick recognition of Angela's familiar silhouette brought relief even before her friend spoke. 'Mind if I come in for a minute?'

'No, I don't mind,' Sarah assured her carelessly, and dropped her head back on the pillow.

Angela swiftly closed the door and tactfully chose not to switch on the light. She felt her way along the bed and Sarah shifted her position to make room for her friend to sit down.

'Sarah . . .' Angela sucked in a deep breath and continued in a guilty rush, 'Ben tells me I was out of line saying what I did, and it's none of my business what you choose to do with your life, and if you think marrying Ben is a good move, well . . . that's your decision, and I'm sorry I butted my nose in and . . .'

'Angela, stop worrying,' Sarah advised as soon as she could get a word in. 'It was just a silly dream. Reaction to the break-up with Julian, I suppose. Ben was here and——' she shook her head over her odd receptivity to Ben's proposal '——I guess I was in the mood to listen. He was nice to me.'

Very nice . . . the way he had held her, looked at her, talked to her, kissed her . . . it hadn't felt like a charade. But how could she trust her feelings after her terrible mistake with Julian?

Angela still sounded uncertain as she pressed on. 'Well, Ben isn't too pleased with me at the present moment. Said I insulted you and he really means to look after you and treat you right.'

'He did look after me tonight,' Sarah conceded with a whimsical little smile. 'But it won't do, Angela. I'd want more from a husband than just money. I'm sorry I led Ben to think I might be interested.'

Angela heaved a huge sigh of relief. 'Well, thank God for that! Not that I wouldn't like you as my sister-in-law, Sarah, but much as I love my brother, I'm damned sure he'd make you a terrible husband. He's quite mad, you know.'

'Mad?' The word recalled her initial doubts about Ben's sanity.

'I don't mean he's off his brain. Far from it. In fact, I guess a lot of people would call him a genius in a quirky kind of way. He's terribly clever but he's hopelessly erratic. Not the type you could ever hope to settle down with and lead any kind of normal existence. He's always on the move. He only arrived back from the States yesterday, and he's sure to take off again once he gets himself married. Even the thought of being pinned down horrifies him.'

Angela's voice suddenly warmed with affection as she added, 'That's not to say he doesn't have any virtues. Ben is wonderfully kind and generous. A real sucker for lame dogs and anybody who's got anything wrong with them.'

That would make sense, thought Sarah wryly. Tonight she had been a lame dog, and that probably explained why Ben had done all he could to make her feel better.

Angela sighed again. 'I'm sorry, Sarah. I've been

prattling on about Ben, when all you care about is Julian. I'm so sorry that . . . is it final?'

Sarah's answer was slow in coming, regret for what had been lost mixing with the bitterness of defeat. 'He'd have to change an awful lot for me to reconsider, Angela, and that's most unlikely. I'd rather not talk about it now.' The tears were gathering again.

'Sure,' Angela said in soft sympathy and quickly rose to her feet. 'I'll go and straighten my brother out. Don't worry about Ben, Sarah. I'll keep him out of your way. You just get a good night's sleep.'

Better for her to keep out of Ben's way too, Sarah thought when she was left alone. She had unwittingly encouraged him tonight, raised expectations that now had firmly to be set aside. She would pack a bag in the morning and catch a train to Mount Victoria after work. Her parents were expecting her . . . with Julian. The least she could do was got home and explain, try to mollify her mother's disappointment.

Mental and emotional exhaustion finally dragged Sarah into sleep. When she rose in the morning, she found that Angela had had the foresight to give her own room to her brother and had set up the foldaway bed for herself in the living-room. Sarah was grateful that she was saved the embarrassment of facing Ben again before she left. She told Angela her plans, asked her to wish

Ben luck with his marriage quest, then hurried out of the apartment before the man himself put in an appearance.

Saturday morning was always busy in the Young Trends department and Sarah was glad to be busy. She enjoyed advising customers on how to co-ordinate their chosen purchase with other mix-and-match garments. She was a good saleswoman, never pressing her suggestions but making sure the customer saw all that could be fancied and bought.

She was still smiling her satisfaction over a very large sale when Ashley Thompson, her best sales assistant, ventured a comment between customers. 'I guess we didn't get the Penny Walker contract.'

Sarah's smile turned into a grimace. 'No. Sorry, Ashley. I didn't feel like talking about it yesterday.'

The girl shared Sarah's own enthusiasm for the young designer's work and showed her disappointment. 'I bet that was Mrs Chatfield's doing.'

'Not all of it,' Sarah answered honestly. Then, on a more diplomatic note, 'No one accepts change easily, Ashley.'

Sarah suddenly caught sight of Julian striding purposefully towards her. Her mouth compressed to a thin line that barely held in a surge of rebellion. He wore a contemptuous air for the whole female fashion business. However, before he reached Sarah, she was approached by another customer for advice and she took secret satisfaction in the fact that Julian was forced into waiting for her attention.

But he didn't wait. In his arrogantly demanding way he broke into the conversation and directed that the customer go to Ashley, who was still at the sales desk. Rather than involve a customer in an unpleasant scene, Sarah let Ashley take over, but it took all her control to turn to Julian with an air of sang-froid.

'Another urgent and important matter, Julian?' she bit out.

'The question of our future is certainly urgent and important,' he retorted, a cold, stiff anger behind every word.

'We have no future, Julian. I thought I made that clear yesterday.'

'That's ridiculous, Sarah. We've got too much going for us for you to turn your nose up at it, so just climb down from your high horse and start talking sense.'

Her hackles rose to a dangerous peak. He was doing it to her again, putting her in the wrong instead of recognising his own shortcomings. 'Why don't *you* climb down, Julian?' she said with false sweetness. 'I'm rather sick of that little exercise.'

'Me climb down?' he snorted impatiently. 'I don't have to. It's you who's in a childish pet! It's about time you got your priorities straight, Sarah. If you're going to marry me——'

'But I'm not going to marry you,' she said flatly, aware now that he was never going to see her point of view.

His face contorted with frustration and Sarah could almost hear the grinding of teeth as he snarled, 'I'm not going to beg, Sarah. Please reconsider before it's too late.'

It cost her considerable effort simply to remain civil, but she tried to moderate the tone of her reply. 'I'm sorry, Julian, but we see things too differently. Thank you, but I really don't want another chance. It's better for both of us if we go our separate ways. Now, please excuse me. I have customers to attend to.'

He grasped her arm as she started to turn away and his fingers bit in hard. 'Stuff the customers!'

'Let go of me, Julian,' she demanded, her eyes as cold as a winter storm.

His mouth thinned into a cruel line.

Sarah barely controlled a tremor of fear. 'This is my territory and I'll have you ejected if you start making trouble,' she warned.

A hand suddenly clamped on Julian's arm. 'This guy giving you trouble again, Sarah?'

Startled, she looked up to find Ben Haviland standing at her shoulder. He looked impressive, dressed up in a dark business suit, spotless white shirt and a smart tie, and his genial face was set in beetling disapproval of Julian. Relief swept through Sarah. It felt good to have Ben beside her, ready to champion her cause.

'Nothing I can't handle,' she declared, confident that the situation would now be very quickly resolved.

Julian let her go and wrenched his arm out of Ben's grip. 'Don't think you can manhandle me in a public place. I'll have you up for assault,' he threatened.

'Then leave Sarah alone,' Ben said reasonably.

'Just who do you think you are?' Julian snarled, bristling for a fight.

Another misjudgement, Sarah thought in dismay. Julian's ego had taken too much of a bashing, and pride was forcing him to make a stand, despite the unequal odds. And customers were gathering around, staring curiously at them, listening to all that was going on. The need to end the unpleasant scene pounded through Sarah's mind and she pounced on the one sure solution. She could explain to Ben later, she assured herself as she consciously leaned against him.

'I'm sorry, Julian, but this is the man I'm going to marry,' she declared without batting an eyelash.

Julian's jaw sagged.

'You are?' Ben said, hopeful delight leaping into his eyes as he glanced down at her in surprise.

'There are conditions,' she hissed out of the side of her mouth. She hadn't realised he would look so eager and pleased. A flock of uncertainties played havoc with her heart.

'You can't marry him,' Julian thundered.

Sarah dragged her attention back to her ex-fiancé. He was glaring at her in terrible anger. She hoped the course she had so impulsively taken was not going to backfire on her and inspire an even worse scene.

'Yes, I can,' she insisted with ringing conviction, alarmingly aware that she had made her bed and now must lie in it, at least until Julian departed.

'She certainly can,' Ben said even more emphatically, his arm curving around Sarah's shoulders in pleased possession. 'This is great, Sarah,' he beamed down at her, blissfully ignoring Julian's presence. 'I told Angela she was wrong. Had to be. You and I . . .'

'I don't believe it!' Julian raged. 'Yesterday you were marrying me. Who is this guy, anyway?'

'Don't you know when to give up?' Ben shot at him. 'You had your chance and blew it. You're twenty-four hours too late. Now you haven't got any business here any more, and Sarah and I have arrangements to make, so just be a good chap and shove off. I don't want to hurt you.'

Julian's fists clenched as he glared hatred at both of them. The argument had drawn even more customers, fascinated with what would transpire next. Sarah's heart plummeted. What had possessed her to use Ben to fend off Julian? It had seemed like the inspiration of the moment until Ben had taken her literally at her word. Now she was going to have to find some way to square it with him.

'What time do you finish work, Sarah? Twelve o'clock?' he asked eagerly.

'Yes,' she replied, and was appalled to see Frances Chatfield's tight face of authority boring towards them. Julian was still standing his ground, furious and flummoxed. The situation was getting worse by the second.

'Then I'll pick you up the minute you're finished and we'll whiz off to Mount Victoria,' Ben said with satisfaction.

'I have to talk to you first, Ben,' Sarah got in hastily.

Julian exploded into absolute outrage. 'You're taking him up to meet your parents?' He shook a furious finger at her. 'That's it, Sarah! You're finished!'

His face was white. He was almost frothing at the mouth. To Sarah's intense relief he flung himself away, shouldering customers aside. He ran straight into Frances Chatfield. The bump he gave her knocked her to the floor. She gave a little cry of horror and distaste as she went down, and customers quickly gathered around to help her up. When she reappeared on her feet, the expression on her face would have turned Medusa to stone.

Sarah glanced up at Ben to find his attention focused entirely on herself and apparently unaware of any disturbance, but Sarah was instantly and forcefully imbued with the principle that discretion was the better part of valour. She spoke with sharp urgency. 'You'd better go, Ben. We can't talk now.' Time to explain to him later.

'No problem,' he said. 'Just tell me which exit you use.' He gave her no time to answer, his words tumbling on in happy anticipation. 'Better make it George Street. I'll go and buy a car straightaway. What do you fancy, Sarah? A Porsche? Jaguar? Ferrari? You'd look good in a Ferrari.'

A Ferrari? Her mind boggled for a moment and into that fraction of a pause sliced the waspish voice of Frances Chatfield.

'Ben Haviland! Finally putting in an appearance! And to find you in the midst of a disgraceful brawl is precisely what I'd expect.'

Ben's jaw dropped. His face stiffened in shock as he turned to meet the flinty gaze of Sarah's immediate superior. 'Frances!' The name was a strangled sound of horror.

'Yes. It's me.' It was a venomous hiss. The supercilious expression that Frances Chatfield usually wore had come unstuck and for the first time Sarah saw naked emotion glittering in her cold, beady eyes. The sight wasn't pretty. It gave

Sarah a crawly feeling down her spine.

Ben's face had gone white. He threw a hunted look at Sarah. 'Got to go. Wait for me, Sarah. At twelve o'clock. I'll be there.'

He was backing away even as he spoke in agitated bursts. His eyes kept darting at Frances as if he expected her to attack him. He threw one last look of frantic appeal at Sarah, then plunged off down the aisle to the nearest exit.

Frances Chatfield's mask of cool sophistication slipped back into place. She gave Sarah a look of scathing superiority. 'May I suggest, Miss Woodley, that as head of this department you show a very poor example by neglecting the firm's business in order to conduct your private affairs? I shall be giving a full report of this disgraceful incident. You deserve to be demoted. I will do my best to see that justice is done.'

Her voice dripped with acid scorn as she added, 'As for Ben Haviland, he is irresponsible, unreliable, and a reckless, amoral scoundrel, and it shows extremely poor judgement on your part to have become involved with him in any way whatsoever.'

With a disdainful lift of her chin she swung on her heel and sailed back to her own department. Sarah had to restrain an extremely childish urge to poke out her tongue. Any sympathy she might have felt for Frances Chatfield over Julian's nasty knock had been more than nullified by the mean vindictiveness of the woman. Not only had she spitefully sabotaged the Penny Walker contract, but there was no doubt that she would indeed do her best to see that Sarah lost her position.

It wasn't fair! Although it was probably her own fault, Sarah conceded grimly. If she hadn't been a blind idiot over Julian . . . if she hadn't brought Ben into the argument this morning . . . and how was she going to undo that?

A group of giggling teenagers caught her eye. They had been the group closest to the whole scene and obviously had been thoroughly entertained by it. One of them broke away and skipped over to Sarah as the others giggled at her audacity.

'Don't take any notice of that old battleaxe,' the girl advised. 'We reckon you should take the Ferrari and go.'

And before Sarah could make any comment, the group surged away, throwing cheeky backward glances as they convulsed with laughter. Sarah wished she could laugh, but what had started as a stupid impulse had finished up with far from funny consequences.

Now she had to face up to Ben and tell him she hadn't meant what she said. If he really did go off and buy a Ferrari . . . well, that wouldn't really be her fault, would it? Life was suddenly very complicated. And what was Ben's connection to Frances Chatfield that she should have such a shattering effect on him?

The name hadn't startled him last night when Sarah had told him about the conference. But Chatfield was Frances's married name. If Ben had known her . . . Sarah recalled that Frances had been Frances Upshot ten years ago and she wasn't really old. About thirty-eight. Could she have been the woman who had niggled Ben with more and more demands until he had bolted? She certainly was the type, and he had certainly bolted when confronted by her.

Sarah could not help chuckling over the incident in retrospect. Ben had taken to his heels as if threatened by a ravening wolf. He would have fought Julian, or any man, without turning a hair, but faced with Frances . . . The irony of the situation suddenly struck her—Julian and herself, Ben and Frances. Maybe she and Ben should team up to protect each other against the tyrants of the world. 'Take the Ferrari and go.' But that was being hopelessly fanciful, Sarah thought with a heavy sigh.

She glanced at her watch. Nine-fifty-six. Two more hours before she could set Ben straight. She hoped he wouldn't be too angry with her when she explained that she couldn't marry him after all. No, he wouldn't be angry, she decided. He'd understand. But she felt awful about disappointing him again.

CHAPTER FOUR

SARAH was not familiar with Ferraris, but when the ultra-sleek red sports car pulled into the kerb near the George Street exit of the store, its sophisticated lines left her in no doubt as to its identity. It shocked her. She hadn't really believed that Ben would do it, or even could do it. It didn't seem possible that anyone could just go and buy a Ferrari off the rack, so to speak. But there was Ben in the driver's seat, tooting the horn and waving her forward with hurry-up gestures.

She snapped herself out of the incredulous daze and moved. Ben had the passenger door open for her by the time she reached it and she passed him the overnight bag she had packed. He heaved it on to the back seat and grinned happily at her as she dropped into the low-slung, beautifully moulded leather seat.

'Like it?' he asked, reaching across for her seat-belt and fastening it for her.

'How did you get it?' The question was still whirling through her mind.

'A sale is a sale. I simply told them if they wanted to sell it, it had to be ready for me to hit the road by

71

a quarter to twelve.' And he proceeded to hit the road, moving smoothly into the stream of traffic heading down George Street.

'But ... but how did you pay for it?' She still couldn't believe it, even though she was actually riding in the car.

'Credit card, of course,' he smiled, as if any old credit card could buy a Ferrari. 'Hope your mother likes chocolates. And I didn't know what your father's favourite drink is so I bought him a good bottle of whisky, a good bottle of cognac and a good bottle of port.' He flashed her a self-satisfied grin. 'How's that?'

Sarah felt even more awful. He had done all this for her because she had said she was going to marry him and now ... Now she had to tell him it had been a stupid, defensive lie. 'You shouldn't have done that, Ben,' she began in a very small voice, but Ben didn't give her time to continue.

'No trouble. I thought your mother would like to see a ring on your finger, too. I should have got your finger size but I didn't want to run the risk of running into Frances again ...' His mouth set in a grim line and he gave a brief shake of his head. 'I'd sooner face piranhas. Or crocodiles. That woman is a viper, Sarah.'

'You don't have to tell me that,' Sarah said with feeling. 'I've had ten years of working under her.

She's the Frances Chatfield I told you about last night.'

'Chatfield? You mean she's married?'

'Widowed.'

'That'd make sense,' Ben said grimly. 'She probably poisoned her husband like she poisoned my dog.'

'She did that?' Sarah was shocked, yet on second thoughts she didn't have much difficulty in believing that Frances Chatfield could poison a dog. 'Was she the woman who almost got you to marry her, Ben?'

'She's the one. God knows, I was a terrible fool to ever get so deeply involved with her. Somehow she used to keep twisting me around until I was doing all sorts of things I hated, just to please her.'

His tone was full of disgust and Sarah instinctively rushed to offer mitigating circumstances. 'She is a good bit older than you, Ben. About four years.'

'Really?' He looked astonished for a moment but the grimness quickly returned. 'She's a liar, too. Can't stand liars. I remember the way she dismissed the whole thing when Tramp died. Couldn't trust her after that.'

He threw Sarah a look of sharp concern. 'I don't like the thought of you working under her, Sarah. Machiavelli had nothing on that woman. The sooner we get you your own boutique the better.'

Her own boutique . . . marriage to Ben . . . Sarah was jolted back to her own problems. While she was in complete sympathy with Ben where Frances Chatfield was concerned, she still couldn't marry him just to escape from her work situation. Yet she had said she would marry him! How was he going to react to her confession when she told him the complete truth?

'You know, Sarah,' he said in a soft, confidential tone, 'I'd got to the point where I thought I was hopeless at picking women. That's why I got Angela on to the job. But I feel really good with you. No nasty prickles down the spine at all.' And he smiled at her, an oddly touching smile of happy approval.

It was on the tip of her tongue to say that she felt comfortable with him too, but she caught the words back in time. She had to make her position clear to Ben. Right now. She couldn't let this misunderstanding go on any longer, but it was terribly difficult to find the right opening. He had been so nice to her, was still being nice to her, and the stark truth was . . . she liked his niceness. But that was no excuse for postponing the inevitable.

'Ben . . .' she began determinedly.

'Yes?' He flashed an encouraging smile at her.

Shame squeezed her heart. At least, Sarah thought it was shame. It had to be shame. What else could it be? She forced herself to go on. 'About what I said this morning . . .'

Ben chuckled. 'Never felt more relieved in my life. I told myself I was only dropping in to apologise to you for taking advantage of what Angela reckoned was emotional rebound, but the fact is, Sarah, I was really hoping Angela was wrong. I just couldn't let it go. Like I said last night . . . you and I are something else again.'

The pleasure in his voice sent ripples of warmth right down to her toes. Which reminded her of the way Ben had massaged them last night . . . and then kissed her. But she had been off balance last night, common sense insisted. Now, in the clear light of day, she couldn't possibly consider marrying Ben. Even his sister had told her he would make a terrible husband.

She tried again. 'Julian was making it very difficult this morning, Ben. When you came——'

'You suddenly saw the light,' Ben popped in cheerfully, then grinned at her. 'You don't have to explain, Sarah. The way we agreed on how a marriage should be . . . we're in absolute harmony about it. I guess I should thank Julian for reminding you of how compatible we are.'

'Well . . . er . . . I'm not too sure about that, Ben,' Sarah put in tentatively, having been floored once again.

Were they compatible? They certainly seemed to have a lot of attitudes in common, but she hardly knew the man. She had only met him last night! Events had moved so fast that she could hardly keep up with them, but she had to make a stand now. The problem was that everything she said got twisted against her. Perhaps a more indirect approach might help.

'What about the woman that Angela found for you?'

'No trouble. We'll square that up at the first opportunity.' He chuckled again. 'I sure am going to enjoy seeing Angela's face when we arrive back tomorrow and tell her we're getting married.'

There was no way out of it except to be brutally blunt, Sarah decided, much as it pained her to disappoint him. 'Ben, what I said about marrying you this morning . . . well, I was in a bind at the time and . . . er . . . maybe I went too far . . .'

'Not at all. Quite all right. Glad you did. Best way to deal with that chap. Very positive,' Ben said admiringly.

He certainly wasn't making it easy for her. Sarah took a deep breath. 'Ben, I can't just marry you off the cuff, so to speak. You must understand that . . .'

'It's all right, Sarah,' he cut in quickly. 'You did say there were conditions and that's fair enough.'

Conditions! Sarah grasped that concept as though it was her last lifeline. 'That's right,' she agreed. All she had to do was think up some conditions that Ben would find unacceptable and he would withdraw from the idea of marrying her.

'What are the conditons?' he asked.

'Well ... umm ...' Did she really want to put him off?

'Don't worry. I'm sure we can work them out to our mutual satisfaction.'

His confidence warned her that they would have to be pretty tough. 'I'm ... er ... I need to think about them.'

'Sure. Take as much time as you like,' Ben said kindly. 'We've got the whole weekend. You just tell me when you're ready.'

Sarah breathed a quiet sigh of relief. The weekend with her parents would surely produce the answers to the questions that had been bombarding her heart and mind. She would get a much more rounded view of Ben Haviland's personality and character, and maybe she would be able to sort out precisely how she felt about him and his proposal of marriage. And it wouldn't really be wasting his time even if she did end up rejecting him. After all, he could still go back to Angela's candidate.

Sarah gradually relaxed. She had the rest of today and tomorrow before she had to think of something, and something was bound to come up that would make Ben see they weren't suited. Meanwhile, his presence would surely help her through a difficult weekend. Her mother could hardly bemoan the loss of Julian when a larger-than-life Ben Haviland was at Sarah's side.

They left the city behind and Ben purred the Ferrari along the F2 Freeway towards the Great Western Highway. 'Great car, isn't it?' he remarked. 'I had one the last time I was in Italy and really enjoyed driving it.'

'It's a marvellous car,' Sarah agreed, but his comment about Italy started her thinking more about him. Always on the move, Angela had said, and he had just come back from the States. It was an expensive way to live. And this car bought on a credit card . . . 'How do you make all your money, Ben?' she asked curiously. 'I know you said selling ideas, but what kind of ideas?'

'Oh, things that strike me as handy, or fun, or more efficient. It's simple really. Take, for example, the ring pulls on cans of drink. Now that was a brilliant idea. Then there's the Cabbage Patch dolls. Very smart concept there, making dolls like real babies with adoption papers and everything. It's coming up with a convenience, or something with great market appeal. That's what sells.'

'And what's the latest thing you've come up with?'

He chuckled. 'The Cyli-Silo.'

'You mean that cylindrical puzzle thing that's driving everyone crazy?'

'Uh-huh. Thought of it while I was playing computer games. Kind of thing you can fiddle with on a bus or a train, and with enough fascinating challenge in it to hook anyone from schoolkids to bank managers.'

'That's fantastic, Ben,' Sarah said, somewhat awed by his ingenuity.

'Mmm. Trouble is, it took off even better than I thought it would, and that's why I've got the tax problem. Worth millions. Literally,' he moaned.

It suddenly struck Sarah that a lot of women would jump at the chance to marry a man such as Ben. Not only was he wealthy, but he was reasonably young and very attractive as well. That he was still a footloose bachelor could only be attributed to his wariness of being trapped into a relationship where he couldn't call his soul his own. There was no doubt that her main attraction for him was the fact that she had expressed the same wariness.

But while she might want the freedom of her own individuality, Sarah did not want the freedom of being left entirely alone while her husband skipped off around the world for months or years at a time. She wondered how Ben would react to the condition that they actually spend their life together. Sarah looked at him consideringly. He certainly appeared happy enough to spend this

weekend with her, even though it meant sharing it
with her parents.

They reached the outskirts of Katoomba, the
commercial heart of the City of the Blue Mountains, and instead of keeping on the highway Ben
took the scenic route that bypassed the business
centre. 'Long time since I've been up here,' he
remarked with a smile that appealed for her
indulgence. 'I'd like to take in the view if you don't
mind.'

'Good to miss out on the traffic,' Sarah nodded.

No matter how many times she had seen the
popular tourist spots like Echo Point where the
stony peaks of the Three Sisters formed a unique
landmark, Sarah never failed to be enthralled by
the grandeur of the Blue Mountains—mountains
and valleys rolling on and on as far as the eye could
see, all wrapped in the distinctive blue haze caused
by the eucalyptus oil projected into the atmosphere
from the massed growth of millions of eucalyptus
trees.

At one of the more spectacular vantage points
along the road, Ben pulled the Ferrari over to the
verge and parked. 'This is as good a place as any,'
he said, his eyes sparkling at Sarah as he reached
over to the back seat for his suit jacket. He drew a
small velvet bag from one of its pockets. 'I got a few
rings on approval since I wasn't sure of your finger
size. I hope one fits. And if you don't like diamonds

we can change it for something else on Monday.'

While Sarah's mind staggered under the pressure of this new development, Ben unwrapped a magnificent diamond solitaire ring. She was too mesmerised by the size of the blue-white stone even to think of protesting when Ben took her left hand and slid the ring on to her third finger.

It stuck on her second knuckle. 'Too small,' Ben muttered, and slid it off again. 'Maybe the next one.'

Sarah finally pulled herself together enough to stop him from unwrapping another small fortune. 'Please don't, Ben. I can't accept it. Not when . . . when we haven't got things properly settled yet,' she added hastily. Her eyes lifted to his in anxious appeal. 'Mum and Dad will think it's too rushed anyway. It'll raise questions, Ben. Truly it will.'

He frowned. 'Didn't think of that.' He heaved a disappointed sigh. 'I guess the ring can wait until tomorrow. But, Sarah . . .' his eyes were suddenly questioning hers with a very warm appeal, 'Sarah, I can't put this off any longer.'

Sarah told herself it was relief that prompted her ready acceptance of his kiss, but she couldn't fool herself that it was relief that made her respond to it. Not in the way she did, because she forgot all about everything, and every bit of sense she had was cut off for the duration, swamped by a galloping range of sensations that aroused a compelling desire for more. And the odd part was, it was not a demanding assault on her mouth, more an invitation to explore together, except that it was Ben who initiated and she who followed his subtle escalation of sensual excitement.

It took her some time to focus her eyes on him when Ben finally drew away. Her breathing was decidedly ragged. Every nerve in her body seemed to be jangling with heightened awareness. Her lips quivered with the need for the seductive pressure to be renewed. In a daze she saw Ben give a slight shake of his head, heard him drag in a deep breath. Then he slumped back into his own seat, decisively separating himself from her. He picked up her hand and stared down at it for long tension-filled moments as his fingers stroked over hers. Again he shook his head.

'That's pretty strong medicine. Very strong,' he muttered, then turned to her with a rueful smile. 'You sure do give a man a shot in the heart, Sarah.'

An embarrassed little laugh broke out of her own sense of incredulity. 'You have quite a forceful aim yourself, Ben.'

The smile split into a delighted grin. 'Didn't I say we'd be good together? And it's got nothing to do with perfume, either. Just great chemistry. Great!' he repeated with relish.

He put her hand back on her knee, patted it indulgently, then switched on the powerful engine and eased the Ferrari back on to the road. For the twenty minutes or so that it took to get to Mount Victoria, Sarah's wits were in a hopeless muddle. She had never given much weight to chemistry. She had always believed that it was emotional involvement more than physical attraction that made a kiss special. But she wasn't emotionally involved with Ben Haviland. How could she be? There hadn't been enough time!

It was only when Ben asked for street directions that Sarah made a concentrated effort to pull herself together. The moment they arrived, explanations would have to flow thick and fast. She hadn't even telephoned her mother to say that Julian wasn't coming. She had meant to call from Central Railway before catching the train but ... well, Ben Haviland certainly presented a *fait accompli*, and his personality was strong enough to dim any other considerations.

The street was a narrow one, so she directed Ben to park in the driveway. He was out of the car before Sarah had undone her seat-belt, and held her door open for her to alight. Then he worked some mechanism to push the seat forward so that he could lift out her overnight bag. He was just straightening up when her mother came shooting out of the house to greet them.

'Sarah! My goodness! What a lovely car! And you must be Julian,' she added, beaming an indulgent welcome at Ben.

'I'm afraid he's . . .' Sarah began, only to be cut off by her father who had followed on his wife's heels.

'Sarah! At long last! It's about time you turned up to see us with your young man,' he chided good-humouredly. He thrust a hand out to Ben. 'Pleased to meet you.'

Ben cheerfully shook the offered hand, an affable grin on his face as he replied, 'Pleased to meet you too, Mr. Woodley. And you, Mrs Woodley. But I think I ought to tell you I'm not Julian.'

'Not . . .' Martha Woodley turned a bewildered look on her daughter.

'I was just going to tell you, Mum. This is Angela's brother, Ben Haviland. He's . . . er . . . just come home from overseas and is staying in the apartment with us at present. And I—I've broken my engagement to Julian.'

To Sarah's relief, Ben took it upon himself to continue the explanations. 'He wouldn't have made Sarah happy, Mrs Woodley. Not the sort of chap you'd want as a son-in-law at all. In fact last night I think he would have hit her if I hadn't been there to stop him and send him on his way.'

'Hit Sarah?' her mother said in shocked tones.

'I didn't think he could be a good type, Martha,' Jack Woodley observed critically. 'Not when he works for the taxation department.'

'The taxation department!' Ben's face reflected his own deep displeasure with that particular arm of government.

'One of the higher echelons, Sarah told us. Getting after people who have earned their money the hard way. Never did think it was much of a job.'

'Couldn't agree more,' Ben said with feeling. 'A man like that is capable of anything. And that was just how he was treating Sarah. Capable of anything!'

'Not strong on family, either,' Jack Woodley added, showing his discontent with his daughter's ex-fiancé. 'He should have come to meet us before this. Sarah was always making excuses for him. Didn't even ask me for Sarah's hand. Not that it's done much these days, but it's a discourtesy, you know,' he said to Ben.

'Ah . . .' said Ben, shooting Sarah a grateful look. He stepped over and put his arm around her shoulders. 'I'm glad you mentioned that, Mr Woodley, because I want to tell you here and now, that's the very reason I'm here. Sarah's still thinking about what she wants, but as far as I'm concerned, I'd marry your daughter tomorrow. I want you to know my intentions straight away because I sure would like you to approve of them.'

He gave Sarah's shoulders a possessive hug and his face beamed his pleasure at her parents. 'You've got a great girl here, and nothing would make me happier than to have her as my wife. Knew it as soon as I met her. Hit me like a bolt of lightning. I get all my best ideas that way so I knew I was right.'

'Well . . . well . . .'

Sarah watched her mother struggle for speech and felt a sharp sympathy for her predicament. Ben had a natural flair for taking away anyone's breath.

'Well, you'd better come inside, I've got lunch ready,' she finished weakly.

'Very welcome,' her father added, his initial surprise being overtaken by a definite air of approval.

'Just get some things out of the car first,' Ben said eagerly, giving Sarah a look of happy triumph before releasing her.

He handed her mother the largest box of chocolates Sarah had ever seen. 'Hope you've got a sweet tooth, Mrs Woodley,' he said with an appealing grin.

'My goodness!' She shook her head, just as Sarah had been shaking her head ever since she had met Ben.

He loaded her father up with the bottles of whisky, cognac and port, plus a bottle of French champagne. 'Something to have with dinner, or after it,' he suggested hopefully.

'Glenfiddich! Now there's a great drop of whisky,' her father observed with pleasure. 'I must say I admire your style, my boy.'

The issue of Julian was completely buried, Sarah noted in dazed bemusement as they finally made their way towards the house, and even before they were inside Ben was invited to call her parents Jack and Martha. Her father took Sarah's overnight bag, saying he would put it in her room, and offered to show Ben to his, clearly delighted at the prospect of having him stay with them. Sarah followed her mother into the kitchen to help with the serving of lunch.

'He's very nice, Sarah. Very nice,' she enthused.

And what could she say to that except agree? Sarah had the distinct impression that Ben Haviland was an unstoppable steam-roller, and the way things were going, some extremely nimble foot-work would be required if she was to get out of marrying him. On the other hand, would marriage to him be such a bad move after all? Sarah felt very, very confused.

CHAPTER FIVE

HE hadn't put a foot wrong. Not so much as a toenail. If he had set out to woo her parents into thinking he would make the perfect son-in-law he couldn't have put on a more effective act. And yet it hadn't appeared to be an act. Not once throughout the whole afternoon and evening had Ben Haviland said or done anything that could be perceived as false or forced.

He had answered her parents' curiosity about him over lunch with open good humour. They had been as impressed as Sarah with his inventive ideas and marketing success. Her father had triumphantly produced a Cyli-Silo, all worked out through trial and error, and listened with fascination as Ben explained how he had had the idea.

When invited to potter round the garden, he pottered quite happily, showing interest in all that her parents showed him. Dinner had been a totally relaxed family affair, and when the inevitable question was asked if he played cards, Ben delighted her parents by challenging them to select any card game at all and he would give them a run for their money. He partnered Sarah against her parents at bridge with a boyish enthusiasm that kept them playing until midnight, and no one could have doubted that he had enjoyed himself immensely.

Sarah heaved another sigh, turned her pillow over, and tried to settle herself more comfortably, but she knew sleep was a million miles away. Her mind was far too active, endlessly revolving the events of the day, examining them from every angle, and getting more confused than ever over the character of the man who was now ocupying the bedroom on the other side of the wall.

She wondered if he was asleep or still lying awake, as conscious of her nearness as she was of his. The way he had looked at her as they had said goodnight ... it was just as well her parents had been present. It was just as well they were in her parents' home, because Sarah wasn't at all sure how she would handle it if Ben started making love to her.

His eyes had been making love to her ever since they had arrived here, continually reminding her of that kiss in the car. Every time he spoke to her, turned to her, over lunch, in the garden, at the dinner table, with every play of the cards, those warm, blue eyes kept dancing with the sure knowledge that it would be good between them. Better than good. Great!

Chemistry, he called it. Strong medicine. And

Sarah had to admit that it was getting stronger with every hour passed in Ben's company. But all the sex appeal in the world would not turn him into the kind of husband she wanted. It was all very well for Ben to be the congenial homebody for one weekend. It probably had a novelty value for a man who was virtually homeless. But for how long could he stick to such a home life? How long would he be happy in it?

In a burst of frustration with her thoughts, Sarah kicked off the blankets and rolled out of bed. She was never going to get to sleep at this rate. She headed for the kitchen. A cup of hot chocolate might help, and if she read one of her mother's magazines for a while . . . anything to get her mind off this treadmill of unanswerable questions.

There was plenty of milk in the refrigerator. Sarah took out one of the cartons, found the tin of Milo, spooned a generous amount of the chocolate-flavoured granules into a large mug, and mixed in the milk. She placed the mug in the microwave oven, set the timer for two minutes and pressed the start button. She watched the ovenplate on its first revolution with a satisfied sense of positive action, then turned away to replace the carton of milk in the refrigerator.

The sight of Ben standing in the kitchen doorway almost startled her into dropping it. He wore only a bath-towel fastened around his hips and his naked torso was every bit as impressively masculine as his clothed physique had suggested.

'Hi!' he said with a semi-apologetic grin. 'I'm glad it's you.'

'I couldn't get to sleep,' Sarah said in an attempt to drag his gaze back up to her face. She hadn't bothered to pack a dressing-gown and her silk nightie not only clung to every curve of her body, but its neckline sliced a deep cleavage almost to her waist. There were a couple of pretty modesty bows stretching across the valley between her breasts, but the way Ben was looking at them, he certainly didn't find them modest.

'I couldn't sleep either,' he echoed rather belatedly, his attention clearly concentrated on other matters as his gaze roved to the lower curves of hip and thigh.

Sarah was suddenly very conscious of the bright fluorescent kitchen light. How transparent was the silk with all those kilowatts beaming through it?

'That sure is a lovely nightie you've got on, Sarah,' Ben murmured appreciatively, then gave his own attire a rueful glance. 'I borrowed this towel from the bathroom. Always sleep in the nude myself. Hope you don't mind.'

Mind? Mind the precarious covering of the towel, or his sleeping naked? What would it be like to go to bed with him? The microwave pinged time-up, dragging her mind off a disturbing array of very physical thoughts.

'I was just making some hot chocolate,' she said with a fluttery wave at the oven. 'Would you like a mug?'

'Sounds good,' Ben nodded and moved forward. 'But don't you bother. Just find me another mug and I'll make it myself.'

'It's no bother,' she said hastily, anxious to keep some distance between them. Her arm swept out to click open the oven door. 'You have this one and I'll ...'

'No, that's yours,' he insisted, and reached for the carton of milk she still held in her hand.

His fingers brushed over hers, her grip slipped and before either of them could save it, the carton dropped on to the floor, spilling milk around their feet. They both swooped down, their heads colliding in the confusion of the moment. Sarah reeled back. Ben clutched her shoulder to steady her, apologising profusely as he scooped the carton upright to prevent any more spillage. 'You sit down. I'll clean this up,' he instructed, blue eyes stabbing concern into hers.

'No. No, I'm all right,' she said somewhat breathlessly. His face was very close to hers and his hand had brushed over her breast to take a better lifting grip under her arm. She almost flung herself away from him, words spilling from her tongue in a wild grab for normality. 'Mum keeps her cleaning sponges under the sink. I'll ... I'll get some to ... for wiping up.'

'I'll help,' he said eagerly, standing with her, placing the carton on the bench and turning on the tap for her to wet the sponges.

He took one from her. Together they squeezed out the excess moisture and then squatted down to mop up the milk. Sarah concentrated hard on the floor but her eyes were irresistibly drawn by the sheer physical attraction of the man. But when she darted a glance up at his eyes it was to find them riveted on the jiggle of her breasts as she swept the sponge over the floor.

She fairly leapt up, ostensibly to rinse out her sponge. He was right behind her, shoulder to shoulder, reaching around her arm to hold his sponge under the tap, too. Neither of them said a word. They bent down again, swishing their sponges around the floor as if racing the clock. Sarah's pulse had gone completely haywire. Her heart was hammering against her chest as she straightened up again. The floor was clean. Clean enough, anyway. They rinsed the sponges and laid them on the sink to dry out.

Sarah waited for Ben to move away. He didn't. His fingers softly stroked the nape of her neck and trailed slowly down the curve of her spine. She shivered. She had to break away from him. Had to, her mind dictated frantically, but he was turning her towards him and her body was weak putty in his gentle hands.

He moved closer, his body swaying against hers, the rough texture of the towel rubbing an electric awareness of every pressure through the thin silk of her nightie. Sarah's mind was jammed by a flood of sensational signals. Only her hands obeyed the dictates of conscience as they plucked in weak protest at his shoulders, but she was unable to stop the gasping sigh of pleasure that stole from her throat as his lips met hers and roved over them. The hungry need inside her instinctively answered his, quickly escalating into a passionate desire for more and more satisfaction.

Only when his mouth left hers to mark out a sensual trail down her throat did Sarah catch her breath both mentally and physically. This had to stop now or there would be no stopping Ben at all. The towel was no hindrance to him. Nor was her flimsy nightie.

The words she tried to form were strangled into an inarticulate cry as his hand found her breast, his palm fanning the silk that moulded the soft, sensitive flesh, moving in a circular rhythm that barely touched her yet teased her nipple into excited prominence. Sarah closed her eyes in passive surrender to the mesmerising pleasure of it.

Then his hand moved further across, fingers tugging at the fragile bows that held her nightie together. Defensive alarms shrieked around Sarah's brain. He would have her completely naked in a minute. She forced the words out. 'Ben . . . no! Please don't!'

They were barely a croak but he heard them. The fingers stopped their gentle tug. A sigh whispered over his last kiss on her throat and he slowly lifted his head. 'You don't want me to?' he asked, a husky reluctance slurring the words. Then he saw the confusion of desire and shame in her eyes and his hand instantly lifted to her cheek in a tender gesture of reassurance. 'It's all right. I'm sorry I—er—got a bit carried away.'

'Yes,' she choked out, all too aware of how nearly she had got carried away herself. Her body was still reacting to his. Never had she been so aroused to such a peak of wanting.

Ben eased a little distance between them. His hands dropped to her hips as if he wanted to pull her after him, but he sucked in a sharp breath and took a step backwards. His gaze fell to the aroused peaks of her breasts, the slight contraction of her stomach as she too breathed in sharply. She spread a hand on his chest in an instinctive warding-off action, yet the heat of his skin invited more touching. It took all her will-power not to run her hand further.

'It's too soon!' she cried, more in conflict with herself than him. Only days ago she had been with

Julian. Her innate sense of morality was shocked at the wanton response Ben had so easily evoked.

'Wrong place,' Ben muttered. He dragged his gaze back up to hers. 'There is something special between us, Sarah. You feel it too.'

A hot flush spread right through her body, confirming the truth of Ben's assertion even as her mind wildly tried to deny it. 'Ben, I don't want— it's getting in too deep.' Her eyes clung to his in frantic appeal. 'I've hardly had a chance to . . . to sort out what our relationship is.'

His face split into a grin of happy anticipation. 'Our relationship is that we're getting married. And it can't be soon enough for me.'

The reminder of her agreement jolted Sarah into an agitated escape from the disturbingly sexual attraction of the man. She paced the length of the kitchen, a turbulent jumble of thoughts storming through her mind. When she turned, Ben was still where she had left him, but his expression was now one of puzzled concern.

'But it's not a loving marriage, is it, Ben?' she shot at him testily. 'It's just a business arrangement that solves your tax problem, and if I go to bed with you, well, that's simply a convenient fringe benefit. Nothing more. And I . . . I don't want to be used like that.'

'Used?' He picked up on the word as if it deeply offended him. 'Is that how you felt just then? That

I was using you?'

The accusation wasn't fair and Sarah knew it. 'I'm sorry.' She shook her head in helpless bewilderment. 'I shouldn't have responded like that. How can it be right? Only last week I was with Julian and . . .'

'Whatever you had with him has nothing to do with us, Sarah. Nothing!' Ben repeated emphatically. He moved, walking purposefully towards her.

Sarah put out an arm to ward him off. 'Please don't start again, Ben.'

He shook his head. 'I can see we've got some talking to do.' She flinched back as he lifted his hands but he gently caught her face and held it still. His eyes bored through the confusion in hers. 'Don't start putting nasty labels on what we just shared, Sarah. It was good. And I sure as hell don't think of making love to you as a fringe benefit. If we never married, I'd still want to hold you and kiss you and make love with you. Don't you feel the same way?'

'I . . . I need time to be sure,' she protested, even while she was inwardly fighting to stop herself from straining forward into another embrace. Whatever it was . . . the intimacy of the late hour, their state of undress, the immediacy of contact . . . it was all playing absolute havoc with her nerves. 'Please, could we sit down at the table and get a few things sorted out?' she asked, desperately needing a breathing space in order to think straight.

The hurt disappointment in his eyes stabbed her with guilt, yet what else could she have said or done? It was against her whole nature to plunge recklessly into a physical affair. She had never believed in casual sex and couldn't bring herself to accept it now, no matter how strong the temptation.

Reluctantly he let her go and pulled out one of the kitchen chairs for her. 'You sit down, Sarah. I'll bring you your drink.'

She had forgotten all about the mug of hot chocolate in the microwave. She felt so shaky it was a relief to sink on to the chair and let Ben serve her. He took his time, reheating her drink and making one for himself. To her further relief he offered her an apologetic smile as he took the chair opposite her.

'I didn't mean to rush you, Sarah. Fact is, I keep forgetting about your involvement with Julian. All I can think of is you and me, and that's a pretty big blind spot.'

Sarah was intensely grateful for his understanding, but she could not let him accept the blame for her own weakness. 'Maybe I've wanted to be blind too, but there are other considerations, Ben,' she started tentatively.

'I realise that. But I want you to know I won't

put any pressures on you, Sarah.' The blue eyes shot her a sharp look of anxiety. 'I wouldn't want to make you unhappy.'

He meant it, Sarah thought, deeply touched by the caring consideration he was showing her. She liked him very much—his openness, his kindness, his easy affability, the way he touched her, kissed her. She really did like him, and it was hard to say the words that had to be said, but she could not keep fooling herself and him any longer.

'Ben, you're not really planning on us living together, are you?' she said slowly. 'I mean, you'll be away a lot, overseas . . .'

He frowned at her, sensing a problem and wary of what it might mean. 'I've always enjoyed travelling but . . .' The frown cleared. 'I'd certainly like a permanent place here that I could return to. We'll buy a home for us, Sarah. Anywhere that'll suit you. I don't mind. I'd like that with you, Sarah. But you'd be free to come and go, just as you like. No prison, I promise you.'

Sarah's heart sank. In her fierce resentment of Julian's treatment of her, she had spouted those terms last night—was it only last night?—yet it wasn't what she wanted of a marriage. She wanted to share much more than a house, and on more than a part-time basis. She sighed and shook her head.

'It's not a house, Ben. I guess what it comes

down to is making a home and having a family, and you see . . .' her eyes begged him to undertstand, '. . . if I married you, we'd never have those things. That's too high a penalty to pay, Ben, even for all you would give me in other ways.'

He looked stunned. So stunned that Sarah was doubly ashamed of having let him commit himself so far before confessing what she now suddenly recognised as her innermost needs. 'I'm sorry. I had no right to say I'd marry you when I can't be the kind of wife you want.'

His expression underwent a lightning change, an urgency snapping into his eyes as his hands threw out an appeal. 'But I do want you! I want you more than any woman I've ever met. And who said we couldn't have children? I'll admit I hadn't thought that far ahead. Hadn't thought of having kids at all. I guess I've been dumb and stupid as well as blind, but that doesn't mean to say I wouldn't like them.'

Her resolution was momentarily shaken by the unexpected concession from him, but the reason behind it could not be overlooked. Ben wanted her, but how long did desire last where there was no commitment of love? 'Children don't fit into your life-style, Ben,' she explained sadly. 'That's why you haven't thought of them. And children need a father who's there for them, not on the other side of the world.'

For the first time he looked really troubled. 'I

think I'd be all right with kids, Sarah,' he said slowly. 'I'd probably have to go on business trips now and then, but I guess I could adjust to . . .'

'No.' The firm negative drew his anxious attention and she gave him a rueful smile. 'You see, Ben? I'm already putting pressure on you to change, to do something you don't want to do and be something you don't want to be. That's precisely the kind of marriage you're trying to avoid, and I don't blame you. I hated that kind of pressure myself. I don't want to do it to you. It wouldn't be fair.'

She pushed herself to her feet, suddenly very tired and a little sickened by all the mistakes she had made. 'I'm the wrong woman for you, Ben. You only need to solve a tax problem. You don't want to be burdened with a wife and children who'd want you to share your life with them. I'm sorry I've wasted your time.'

'Wait, Sarah!'

She had already reached the doorway and the scrape of his chair on the tiled floor sent a shiver down her spine. Her conscience was now clear and she didn't want to get muddled again. For a moment she swayed from pure fatigue, but the strong attraction of the man pulled her gaze back to him. She had to glance up because he was already at her shoulder. His eyes held an anxious tenderness as he lifted his hand to stroke her cheek in a soft salute.

'You haven't wasted my time, Sarah. I've enjoyed being with you and your family, and I'd like to ask for some more of your time.'

'Ben, I'm about ready to drop. What more is there to say?'

'Nothing right now,' he acknowledged and planted a soft kiss on her forehead. 'You go to bed. I want to think about what you've said. Maybe it's what I want, too. Just don't wipe me off yet, Sarah. Promise me that?'

The appeal lifted some of the leaden weight from her heart, but she felt driven to strip him of any false illusions. 'Ben, there'll always be other women you can make love with.'

'But will I ever forget what I might have had . . . with you?' he asked seriously.

'Sooner or later it'd be a prison for you. Don't forget that.'

He looked so disturbed, like a little boy who had just been slapped in the face with the hard realities of grown-up life. Sarah reached up and kissed his cheek on a wave of tender affection. 'Goodnight, Ben,' she murmured, then hurried off to her bedroom before he got any other ideas.

'Sarah . . .'

The hoarse roughness of the whispered call scraped over her heart. It seemed to express so much of what she was feeling herself, so much that had been so close, almost within reach, a promise that shimmered so enticingly, but a mirage nevertheless. She clutched at her door-jamb, needing its physical support as well as the reminder that life was full of doorways and some were better left closed. With a regret that was painfully intense, she looked back at the dark silhouette framed by the kitchen light. An arm was stretched out to her. It slowly fell.

'Goodnight, Sarah.'

The soft benediction had a ring of finality to it. She did not answer. She stepped inside her room and closed the door. Her eyes brimmed with tears as she laid her head despondently on her pillow. There had been something special between her and Ben, some deep affinity that had never been reached with Julian in all the months they had been together. As she drifted into sleep, her heart ached for what she might have had with Ben Haviland if Fate had shaped their goals in life to a matching end.

CHAPTER SIX

SARAH slept late. When she awoke she wished she had slept even later, or even, not woken up at all. There was nothing about this day she wanted to face. She winced at the thought of facing her parents' pleasure in Ben, and mentally shied away from the emotional strain of facing Ben himself. Tomorrow would begin another round of confrontation with Frances Chatfield's spite at the store. And then what was ahead of her? A big, fat zero! Sarah was not even sure she wanted to face up to the rest of her life.

But that was being unnecessarily defeatist, she told herself as she pushed herself out of bed. Who could tell what might turn up in the future? Hadn't Ben burst into her life like a bolt from the blue, shaking everything up? And at least she didn't have Julian to contend with any more. As incredible as it seemed, she no longer felt even the slightest twinge of regret for the loss of that relationship. And that undeniable fact brought a heavy frown of self-examination to Sarah's brow as she dressed.

She couldn't have loved Julian. There had certainly been a time when she had felt herself in love with him, and she had clung on to that notion in the teeth of one disillusionment after another until the last thread of emotional involvement had been bitten through. They had seemed so well suited to each other, enjoying the same kind of activities and finding a mutual satisfaction in the life-style they had planned for the future. Was that why she had clung so hard?

Perhaps she had it all wrong. Perhaps those things didn't matter as much as how well two people reacted together. On the surface, she and Ben weren't suited at all, yet . . . why did she feel so right with him? So right that she could never have been satisfied with the kind of psuedo-marriage he had proposed.

If she couldn't have his children . . . Sarah shook her head over the way that had slipped out last night and become one of the conditions of marrying him. It had surprised her even when she had said it. She simply did not know Ben Haviland well enough to say that she loved him. Or even well enough to fall in love with him. But she wished . . .

Sarah dragged her mind back from such futile thoughts and gave her hair a hard brushing. She carefully applied the complementary make-up to the casual fashion outfit she was wearing. Dark, plum-coloured slacks were topped by a loose-weave sweater that featured a daring design of plum-roses entwined with indistinct, sea-green foliage and wafts of dark mauve in the background. Sarah was pleased with the effect and felt satisfied that her appearance presented an air of being all together, even if she was a total mess inside.

She found her mother in the kitchen, preparing the usual Sunday roast dinner. 'Sorry I'm late up, Mum, but don't worry about breakfast. I'll just have a cup of coffee,' she said quickly in the hope of avoiding a fuss.

Martha Woodley sighed and shook her head. 'No wonder you're so thin.'

Sarah smiled at her mother's plump figure. 'Not thin, Mum. Just fashionably slim. Where is everyone?' she added casually.

'Your father's taken Ben for a stroll around the town. What there is of it,' she added, before lifting her eyes to her stubbornly single daughter. 'He's very nice, Sarah. He fits in so well, just like one of the family.'

'Yes,' Sarah agreed briefly, although the irony of her mother's statement was not lost on her. If Ben was really a family man he wouldn't be the 'maverick' he was. Angela probably knew him better than anyone, and she certainly didn't believe that the leopard could change his spots.

Martha Woodley was not content to let the matter drop. Ben's virtues were pointed out in a steady stream of observations to ensure that her daughter had a full appreciation of them. To Sarah's relief, her mother did refrain from actually suggesting an acceptance of Ben's proposal, but the message was loud and clear.

Sarah did not feel inclined to disillusion her mother over the type of husband Ben would be, so she kept her replies short and non-committal. As it was, she found the conversation depressing and was almost glad when her father and Ben returned. Until her eyes met Ben's and every nerve in her body knotted with tension.

He still wanted her. And she wanted him. Their conflict over the marriage issue had not diminished the desire that had leapt between them last night. If anything, it was now heightened by the short time that was left to them . . . if Sarah did not weaken from the stance she had taken. And she couldn't. She had thought it all through. She had to stand firm and let Ben go his own way or they would both be miserable.

Sarah did not know how she got through the next couple of hours. Her whole body vibrated with an electric awareness every time Ben came near her, so much so that if he touched her she flinched. Her mind could not concentrate on any line of conversation for long and she noted that Ben was similarly distracted. Fortunately her parents had a lot to say and did not remark on their lapses.

She ate the meal her mother served but she could not remember tasting any of it. She dropped one of the plates in the kitchen when clearing up, and when Ben stooped with her to pick up the pieces, she literally started to tremble with the force of her emotional turmoil. A sharp edge of broken crock-

ery nicked her finger and she used the minor
wound as an excuse to flee to the bathroom,
desperate to regain some composure.

Her parents always went to their bowling club on
Sunday afternoons so she and Ben were expected to
take their leave straight after lunch. For Sarah it
could not be soon enough. She had to say goodbye
to Ben as quickly and as cleanly as possible, and
even the journey down the mountain in the
intimacy of the Ferrari promised to be pure
torment. There was no future in any relationship
between them. She had to keep remembering that.

Having steeled herself to remain calm and in
control, Sarah managed to act quite normally as
her parents accompanied her and Ben to the car.
She kissed them goodbye and said all that was
expected of her. Then Ben completely threw her by
handing her the car keys.

'You drive, Sarah.'

She looked up at him in startled surprise. Julian
had never allowed her behind the wheel of the Alfa,
and here was Ben inviting her to drive his Ferrari!

'You would like to, wouldn't you?' he pressed,
seeing her uncertainty. 'Most people would, at least
once in a lifetime.'

Once in a lifetime ... Of course! Ben had
prmised not to pressure her and he knew as well as
she did that this afternoon was all that was left to
them. And he was right. She would like to drive a
car like this and she would probably never have

another chance. She nodded, too distressed to speak. He took her arm to steer her round to the driver's side of the Ferrari and this time she didn't flinch at his touch. She welcomed it, wanted it, wished there could be more.

Her mother's shocked voice broke the intimacy of the moment. 'But the car's too valuable, Ben. You can't let Sarah . . .'

'Don't tell me you think men drivers are better than women, Martha,' Ben tossed at her teasingly. 'It's a well known fact that women are more safety-conscious on the road. Besides, I'd probably fall asleep at the wheel after stuffing myself on that great dinner you just cooked.'

'Ben, are you sure?' Sarah asked anxiously as he opened the door for her.

The look he gave her sent a shivery feeling right down her spine. 'I'd be happy for you to drive me anywhere, Sarah. Anywhere at all.'

She had no answer to that. She was much too aware that he was referring to a lot more than driving a car, even a Ferrari. She settled rather nervously into the seat and Ben closed the door on her. Her eyes literally ached as she watched him shake hands with her father and heard both her parents say he would be welcome again at any time. They meant it in all sincerity, and somehow that twisted the knife even further. There was no hope that such a visit would ever be repeated.

As Ben climbed in beside her she wondered how

much having children really meant to her. After all, if she never married she would never have them. But to marry someone where children would be an impediment to their life-style . . . No, she couldn't do it. She would want them. She knew she would, sooner or later, and that wouldn't be fair to the children.

She barely heard Ben's instructions as he explained the basic instruments. His hand had covered hers to take her through the necessary gear changes and a tingling warmth was racing through her veins. She switched on the engine when he told her to and only when she had activated the correct gear did his hand leave hers, fingers trailing softly over her slender wrist before falling away. She concentrated so fiercely on handling the powerful car that she forgot to wave to her parents.

Not that it mattered. They would understand, she assured herself. Driving a Ferrari was a daunting as well as an exciting experience, and it also served to force her attention off Ben. It was bad enough that she could feel him watching her, but she knew it would have been far worse sitting in the passenger seat watching him. She kept her eyes firmly fixed on the road. They had been travelling for some ten minutes before Ben broke the silence between them.

'Relax, Sarah,' he said softly. 'The car won't buck if you hold the wheel less tightly.'

Only then did she notice her clenched grip. It

took a conscious effort to unclench her fingers and, try as she might, she could not fully relax. 'It's . . . it's just getting used to the feel of it,' she excused herself.

'I like the sweater you're wearing,' he suddenly commented, making her even more aware of his continual appraisal.

'It's a Penny Walker,' she said out of the sheer necessity of saying something, anything to inject some normality into the atmosphere of the car.

'Is that some special trade name?'

Sarah snatched at the remark as if it were a lifeline. 'Not yet, but it will be. Penny Walker is a brilliant young designer who's looking for a fashion outlet for her clothes. I was in the middle of persuading the store management to take up a contract with her when Julian pulled his act last Friday.' The bitter memory of defeat put a sharp edge on her tone of disgust. 'Our mutual friend, Frances Chatfield, spiked the whole deal while I was out of the conference room. That woman is so rigidly narrow-minded she simply refuses to acknowledge that any other view could be better than her own. To her, fashion is understated elegance, preferably in neutral or earth colours. The safe things,' Sarah added in scornful contempt.

'Like a steady job,' Ben said in sympathetic understanding.

'Exactly. There's no room in her mind for new

ideas, particularly anything that's totally noncon-
formist. And she's full of jealous spite for anybody
who excels her. She's so terribly wrong about
Penny Walker's designs. Stupidly, blindly wrong!
The young market is crying out for bright,
dramatic clothes that are fun to wear, colours and
combinations that make the wearer feel positive
and individual. In my opinion, Penny Walker will
go to the top once she breaks into the market. She's
so marvellously innovative.'

'Sounds like my kind of person,' Ben said
approvingly.

'Mine too,' Sarah agreed with feeling.

The words echoed in her mind, over and over
again in the silence that followed. They magnified
the strong affinity that leapt so naturally between
her and Ben whenever they talked . . . even when
they didn't talk. The sense of closeness—of mutual
understanding and desires and needs—was almost
overwhelming in the intimate confinement of the
car.

She couldn't let him go, Sarah thought with
sinking desperation. She couldn't bear to send him
away to marry someone else. She had to hold on.
But how could she do that when Ben hated to be
pinned down?

'Do you like dogs, Sarah?'

The quiet question took some time to penetrate
her emotional turmoil. She answered distractedly.
'We had a marvellous dog when we were kids.

Honey. That was her name. She was a Labrador. We all adored her. Even Mum, though Honey used to dig up her garden sometimes.' Sarah suddenly remembered the dog that Frances Chatfield had poisoned. 'Was yours a Labrador?'

'No. Tramp was a Border collie.'

'That must have been awful ... losing him like that. We were terribly sad when Honey died, but at least she'd lived a full and very happy life.'

'Yes. A full life,' Ben murmured.

And there was the catch, Sarah thought despairingly. How could she live a full life with Ben when ...?

'Sarah ...'

Ben's hand slid warmly over her thigh. Every nerve in her body went haywire. She couldn't prevent herself from jerking the wheel in desperate reaction to his touch. The Ferrari went off the road and headed for two solid gum trees before Sarah's vision cleared enough to realise the car had bolted on her. Sheer terror gripped her heart. They were going to crash! She found her foot jammed hard on the accelerator and instantly transferred it to the brake but there was no time to stop. The trees were rushing at them, the car bucking over the rough underbrush as if eager to hurl itself to destruction.

Panic screamed through her head that they were going to die. The grim need to survive billowed over it, insisting that she had to keep her head ... control whatever she could as long as she could.

Somehow she steered a safe passage between the trees but despite a desperate swing of the wheel she side-whacked another just beyond them. The car slewed around, collided with something else, flinging Sarah sideways and then into oblivion.

Ben's voice came spiralling through dark, dizzying pain, forcing an awareness of something, something bad and frightening. Her mind moved sluggishly towards it.

'Sarah! Oh God! Sarah, please wake up. Please!'

She forced her eyes open, needing to see, to know. Ben's face swam in front of her.

'Wass th' matter?' Her voice came out slurred, furry.

Ben heaved a sigh and muttered several vehement words under his breath, all of them unintelligible to her. He was dabbing something at her left temple and it hurt. She lifted a hand to stop him.

'It's OK, Sarah,' he soothed. 'Just a small scalp wound but it's bleeding rather a lot. Can you move your legs?' he asked anxiously.

Legs, she repeated in her mind until the message filtered through the fog and stirred her feet.

'Good girl!'

She heard the deep relief in Ben's voice but didn't understand it. Why was he worried about her legs? It was her head that hurt. She must have hit it on something. Then with a lightning burst of clarity she remembered. The car! She had crashed Ben's Ferrari!

Her eyes opened wide, their focus sharpening on the shattered windscreen that had been pushed outwards. She turned her head and found Ben crouched at the opened door on her side. 'How bad is it?' she cried, her feet already scrambling to get out.

'Don't worry about it,' Ben advised quickly. 'I think you'd better stay sitting down.'

'No! No! Let me out! I'm all right!' she insisted wildly, a rush of guilt driving her to examine the damage.

She virtually threw herself out of the car, defying Ben's protests, and suddenly found she wasn't all right at all. Her head performed dizzying circles and she could not have kept upright but for Ben's strong support. His arms came around her in a steadying embrace and she leaned against him until the world stopped spinning.

'It's only a car, Sarah,' he said gruffly. 'For God's sake! Let me look after you.'

'I'm fine,' she lied, resting her head on his shoulder and feeling a lot more alive as the warmth of his body soaked into hers.

Very slowly and carefully she turned her head so that her gaze could take in the car, and then she stared at it in incredulous horror. The whole chassis was bent into a banana shape. Deeply scored scratches disfigured the gleaming bonnet. The back tyre was flat and misshapen. There was not the remotest possibility that this poor twisted wreck of a car would be driven anywhere. She had just written off a Ferrari!

'Oh, my God!' she gasped, absolutely stricken by the enormity of what she had done.

'Don't worry about it. It's insured. It's no problem to get another car,' Ben insisted.

Her eyes sought his, her own guilt stirring anger at his seemingly careless attitude. 'You shouldn't have touched me like that!'

'I know. I didn't stop to think what I was doing,' he admitted gravely.

'It was irresponsible and ... and ...'

'Completely my fault.'

'I was so uptight about ...'

'I know. Me, too. I couldn't stand it any longer. I had to touch you. Couldn't help myself.'

'Oh, Ben ...'

It was a cry of protest against her own ravening need for him and the force of it shook her weakened system even more. There was no fight left in her, no resistance. She slumped against him and his arms enfolded her in a comforting blanket of warm security.

Sarah was barely aware of time passing, of people milling around them, of voices asking questions. She vaguely heard Ben talking. The thought drifted through her mind that maybe she should stir herself to do or say something but her head was feeling woozy again and it was easier just to let Ben be in command.

The next thing she knew someone was tucking a blanket around her and she was lying down somewhere. She cried out in alarm and a gentle hand stroked her cheek. 'Everything's fine,' Ben assured her. 'We're in an ambulance and we're taking you to the hospital at Penrith for treatment. You got a nasty knock on the head, Sarah.'

'Did I black out again?' she asked anxiously.

He nodded. 'Probably concussion. And shock.' He took her hand and gently fondled it. 'Don't worry about a thing. I'll look after you.'

Tears welled into her eyes. 'I'm sorry about the car, Ben. You shouldn't have let me drive.'

'Nonsense! You're a great driver.' He suddenly grinned at her. 'The way you slid us between those trees ... like threading a needle. Stirling Moss would have been proud of you.'

It won a watery smile from her.

'That's better. I like it when you smile,' he said huskily.

'Ben, will you stay with me? At the hospital?'

'They'd have to use crowbars to pry me from your side.'

'Thank you,' she whispered in heartfelt relief. The thought of being left alone in a big, impersonal hospital was rather frightening. Especially if there was something really wrong with her head, like a fractured skull.

Ben was as good as his word, staunchly refusing to accept the suggestion by various medical personnel that Sarah be left in their care. Even while a doctor examined her eyes and when she was wheeled up to the X-ray department Ben remained at her side. It was an enormous relief when she was pronounced clear of all injury except mild concussion and a slight cut above her left temple. However, the recommendation was that she stay in hospital for a couple of days and Ben wouldn't hear of her disobeying this edict.

'But I've got to go to work tomorrow,' Sarah protested.

'Your health and well-being are more important,' he insisted. 'You'll probably be as weak as water tomorrow. Shock does that to you. I'll get Angela to ring up the store and explain your absence. Angela's very good at fixing things like that.'

Fixing other things too, Sarah thought despondently, like getting a suitable marriage candidate who would leave Ben free to live as he liked. He was holding her hand again. In fact, he had barely let it go throughout all the business at the hospital, and Sarah had taken a great deal of comfort from that steady, silent support. She stared down at the strong fingers enfolding hers, secretly wishing that the link did not have to be broken. It was such a good feeling, having Ben look after her.

'I'm sorry I've been so much trouble to you,' she sighed, knowing that their parting had only been postponed by the accident, and tomorrow would bring a return to the inevitable.

'Sarah . . .'

Reluctantly she dragged her gaze up to his, hoping that he would not see how disturbed she felt at the thought of tomorrow, and all the other tomorrows without him at her side. His eyes searched hers with an urgent intensity that made her heart flutter.

'How many kids would you like to have, Sarah? What I mean is, well, if we're going to have a family, I reckon we ought to have a few, don't you?'

Her heart did more than flutter. It catapulted around her chest. 'You—you want a family?' she choked out.

His mouth curved into a funny little smile. 'I hadn't really considered it until you brought it up last night, but I figure you're right. It's like you said in the car before we crashed, about your dog, Honey, having lived a full life. I suddenly realised that I've been more or less skating over the surface, not touching down anywhere long enough to make any meaningful mark. Then when that tree was looking me in the face I thought, this is it! Your number's up! And you've damned little to show for your thirty-four years.'

Uncertainty shadowed the hope that had sprung into Sarah's mind. 'But to have children just for the sake of leaving behind an extension of yourself . . .'

'Hell, Sarah, I don't have that big an ego! No, I

mean to do the thing right. Be a proper dad to them, like your father. He was telling me all about it this morning.'

'You'd stay at home and not keep travelling?' She still couldn't quite believe he meant it.

He grinned. 'We could make a real home, Sarah. Have a big garden so we could have a couple of dogs for the kids. No reason why a Labrador can't get along with a Border Collie if we get them as pups together.'

He spoke with such eager enthusiasm that Sarah couldn't doubt his sincerity. Right at this moment he did want the family-life future he was picturing, but it was the accident that had really triggered his decision. A brush with death often prompted people into an impulsive resolution to change their ways. When it actually came to living the shiny new life, old habits died very hard.

'And you can still run your boutique because I'll be at home to mind the kids,' Ben concluded with an air of having worked everything out very satisfactorily.

Sarah could not accept that he would be satisfied in the long run. 'But what would you do, Ben?'

'When you're inventing things, it doesn't matter where you are, Sarah. I like fooling around on computers so I'll get a couple to play with. I never have any trouble amusing myself.' The grin came again, sparkling with pure pleasure. 'And then there's the best thing of all ...'

'What's that?'

'I'll be married to you.'

And that was at the heart of it all, Sarah reminded herself. He needed to get married and he wanted her.

His grin faded at her lack of response and his brow puckered with concern. 'Are there any other conditions, Sarah?'

She shook her head and a warm tenderness filled her eyes as she looked at the man who would give her everything she wanted ... at this moment in time. 'I'd love that, Ben. To have the kind of life with you that you described just now. But I can't help feeling that you might regret rushing into such a big commitment. It's not what you wanted before this weekend and ...'

'That's because I needed you to enlighten me,' he said with beaming confidence.

It was too much for Sarah to fight. She wanted to give in, to believe it could all come true. Only a persistent nagging of common sense urged one necessary caution. 'Let's wait a few days, Ben. You might have second thoughts about it all. What with the accident and everything else——' her eyes probed his anxiously '—there've been too many pressures, Ben.'

'If that's what you want,' he agreed reluctantly. 'But I'm not going to change my mind and talking about pressures——' a deeper warmth kindled in his eyes '—Sarah, I know this isn't exactly the best place, but I've been wanting to kiss you all day.'

'Me, too,' she breathed.

And it was quite some time before she breathed again.

When Ben was finally ordered from the hospital room by the night nurse, Sarah felt more confused than ever. Neither she nor Ben had spoken of love, but the way Ben made her feel . . . Sarah was no longer sure of what love was, anyway. She knew in her head that if they married it would be a terrible gamble, but her heart was hopelessly set on taking that gamble—if Ben didn't change his mind.

Maybe tomorrrow he would have second thoughts. Or the next day. Or the next. When he really stopped to think of the restrictions that would be placed on his free-roving spirit, would he take fright and run? It worried Sarah. It worried her more than she liked to admit, but there was nothing she could do but wait and see. And hope.

CHAPTER SEVEN

'SARAH?'

A wave of relief rippled through her at the sound of Ben's voice. She gripped the telephone receiver more tightly, as if the extra pressure could bring him closer to her. The morning in the hospital had seemed endless. She had been woken at six o'clock and from that early hour she had been waiting and hoping for some contact from Ben, wanting reassurance that he was still happy about his proposal.

'Yes, it's me,' she breathed happily. 'And the doctor's checked me over and I'm fine, except for being a bit shaky. How are you?'

'Relieved to hear you're OK. Has a policeman been around to interview you about the accident, Sarah?'

'No.'

'Good! If one turns up, say you don't remember what happened. That's fair enough with concussion. I'll get you off any charge, Sarah. I'll say the tyre had a blow-out and the car ran off the road.'

'But ... that's a lie.'

'Mmm. There's not much justice in you being

123

put through a stupid court case. No one else's car was involved and you were the only one hurt. Please, just say you don't remember what happened, Sarah, and leave the rest to me. It was all my fault, anyway, and I don't want you to be further distressed by it.'

Did he really feel the accident was his fault? In the eyes of the law it might not be, and Sarah squirmed at the thought of a truthful report being read out in court. 'All right, Ben. I'll do as you advise,' she said quickly.

'That's a load off my mind. Now, Sarah,' his tone became briskly purposeful, 'I've got a lot of people to see today so I don't know when I'll get back to you. Maybe not until tonight. Is there anything you need?'

'A fresh change of clothes. If you ask Angela ...'

'Right! No problem. Anything else?'

''No, I don't think so.'

'How's your head? Still aching?'

'No. They keep giving me pills.'

'Good! Keep taking them. Got to fly now, Sarah. 'Bye.'

She felt deflated by the brief, matter-of-fact conversation. Ben wasn't coming to see her until tonight and he hadn't even told he what he was doing. Only slowly did Sarah's common sense rally over her disappointment. Of course Ben would be busy today. He wasn't running out on her. He had

to see about the car and ... and the insurance ...
and ... whatever. There was no need to torment
herself with doubts just because he had seemed
rather brusque on the telephone. Some people
weren't comfortable with telephone conversations.

Nevertheless she felt a lot better when an hour or
so later a hospital aide came in with a lovely basket
of flowers. 'Penny Walker special', Ben had written
on the card, and Sarah laughed with pleasure on
noticing the vibrant colour contrasts of the flower
arrangement. She firmly put aside all her misgiv-
ings about Ben's flightiness. They had something
special going between them, as Ben put it, and the
flowers were a beautiful reminder of how closely
they were attuned to each other.

No policeman came, much to Sarah's relief, but
it was a long day, with nothing for her to do except
think, and the fact that she and Ben had only
known each other for such a short time continued
to prey on her mind. She wanted him with her,
needed him with her, and the evening visiting
hours would not come fast enough.

However, it was Angela who walked into Sarah's
room at seven o'clock, not Ben, and Sarah found
herself feeling oddly embarrassed at her friend's
frank scrutiny.

'Your clothes,' Angela said without any pream-
ble, and placed a plastic carrier bag beside her bed.

'Thanks, Angela. It's very good of you to bring

them. I thought Ben——'

'He's off doing something else. I don't know what mischief he's up to and he won't tell me,' came the slightly acid comment as Angela settled herself on the bedside chair and frowned at Sarah. 'You certainly look all right. I've been wondering all day if that knock on your head has scrambled your brains. Do you feel your mind is clear, Sarah?' she asked doubtfully.

A self-conscious little laugh bubbled out of Sarah's throat. 'I guess it must seem pretty mad to you, taking Ben home with me after what I said on Friday night, crashing his Ferrari . . .'

'I can understand the first part because Julian came to the apartment yesterday and told me what happened at the store.'

'Julian came to the apartment?' Sarah was amazed. She hadn't believed that Julian cared about her so much that he would put himself through another confrontation after the knock she had given him on Saturday. Did he care? Or was the blow to his ego smarting too much for him to put it aside? Sarah smothered a twinge of guilt. Julian had got what he deserved for behaving as he did at the store. And towards her!

'What I don't understand . . .' Angela began again with arch emphasis, '. . . is why Ben has this unshakeable belief that you're going to marry him.'

Unshakeable. A smile grew inside Sarah and

danced into her eyes even before it curved her mouth.

'You're not, are you?' Angela demanded incredulously.

'I'm thinking about it, but not the kind of marriage Ben discussed with you, Angela,' Sarah hastily explained.

Angela stared at her, speechless, then shook her head as if nothing made any sense to her.

'He says he wants to have a family,' Sarah pleaded, wanting her friend to understand. 'A real marriage, not a financial deal, Angela. I know it's all terribly sudden, and I've told him we must have more time to be sure it's what we want, but . . .'

'He'll never do it and you're mad to believe it, Sarah,' Angela said with utter certainty. 'He was going to have a real marriage once before and he ran out on it at the last minute.'

'Ben told me about that. He had a good reason, Angela,' Sarah said with equal certainty. 'This is different. We . . . we understand each other,' she finished limply, since she felt rather self-conscious about confessing her precise feelings about Ben.

'Sarah, I don't think you understand a thing about my brother,' Angela said with weary scepticism. 'Just because he was on the spot to support you when you had a fight with Julian, that doesn't mean he'll stick around to support you for the rest of your life. You simply can't rely on him to act like any normal human being. Look what he did to me this weekend!'

She threw up her hands in exasperation. 'He shot off with you and didn't even bother to let me know what he was up to, or where he was. Which is typical! He just comes and goes as the fancy takes him. I had to put off the meeting I'd set up for him with the woman I'd found, and do some fast talking with her in case Ben changed his mind again.'

'What do you mean, changed his mind again?'

Angela heaved a sigh. 'Well, he told me before he left on Saturday morning that he didn't want anyone else but you, but after what you'd said to me on Friday night, I figured I'd better keep his options open.'

'Well, it wasn't Ben's fault that you decided to second-guess him,' Sarah argued staunchly.

Angela stared at her again, more speculatively this time, and a tide of warmth crept up Sarah's throat and spread into her cheeks. 'I told you it wasn't the money,' she said defensively.

'What's been going on since I saw you last?' Angela demanded to know.

Sarah hesitated for a moment, wondering if it was even possible to explain the subtle and not so subtle shifts of emotion that had taken place in the last three days. But it was clear that she had to try, or Angela would never be in sympathy with the situation. She sucked in a deep breath and plunged into confiding as much as she could to her friend.

Angela looked absolutely dumbfounded by the time Sarah had finished stating her case. 'Well, all I can say is God help you, Sarah, if you've fallen in love with Ben,' she finally commented. 'He's sure to break your heart if you take him on as a husband.'

'I didn't say I'd fallen in love with him. I said——'

'Classic case,' Angela declared gloomily. 'And here I've gone and put my foot in it with Julian.'

'What do you mean, put your foot in it?'

Angela sighed and shrugged as if she was carrying the burdens of the world. 'He seemed genuinely upset over losing you, and when he actually admitted that he had behaved badly, I thought perhaps he was seeing the light and might be prepared to change his ways for you.' Her hands lifted and fell in a helpless gesture. 'So I explained that Ben was my brother whom you'd only just met on Friday night and there was nothing serious between you.'

Sarah grimaced. 'So more than likely Julian will be coming after me again!'

Angela rolled her eyes. 'And he's not going to believe you're attached to Ben. I'm afraid I torpedoed that idea. Julian wanted to know why Ben had gone along with your claim that you were marrying him so I . . .'

'You didn't tell him!' Sarah cried in horror. 'You know Julian works for the taxation department!'

Angela frowned. 'It's not illegal to have a tax-deductible wife.'

'Oh, God!' Sarah groaned. 'It'd be just like Julian to go after Ben and try to make something of it once I tell him I don't want a reconciliation. I've heard him gloat over the way his investigators can get people's finances tied up in legal knots for years. If he does that to Ben because of me——'

Despair gripped her heart. Ben had spelt it out to her, how he hated pressures and being pinned down. It was questionable enough that she had pinned him down with children, but to have him pressured by tax investigators ... It simply wasn't fair to put him through that.

'I can't do it,' she moaned.

'Can't do what?' Angela asked, clearly perturbed by her *faux pas* in saying too much to Julian.

'I can't marry Ben. I'd cause him too much trouble.'

Angela looked even more perturbed. 'Seems like I'm the one causing the trouble,' she muttered in self-disgust.

Sarah heaved a despondent sigh. 'Don't worry about it, Angela. You could be right about our marriage failing, anyway. Ben's probably acting on impulse because he wants me, and I . . .' she took a deep, painful breath, 'I guess I've just been dreaming.'

Angela frowned. 'I don't know, Sarah. Maybe you're the kind of woman Ben could be happy with. He was certainly happy last night. I thought his elation had to do with having persuaded you to marry him, but it could have been more than that.' She shrugged. 'I've been setting myself up as a judge and——'

The shrill ring of the telphone on top of the bedside locker startled both of them out of their joyless introspection. Sarah's heart fluttered in anxious hope as she picked up the receiver. Surely it had to be Ben, but why was he ringing? He had said he would come!

'Sarah?'

There was a note of anxiety in Ben's voice that added to her own. 'Yes, Ben,' she said quickly.

'Did Angela bring the things you wanted?'

'Yes. She's here now.'

'Ah! That's good. Nothing more miserable than being in hospital without a visitor. I can't make it tonight, Sarah, but I'll be there tomorrow to tell you all about it.'

'All right,' she said, but it didn't feel all right. Disappointment was flooding through her. 'Thanks for the flowers, Ben,' she added flatly.

'I had expert advice on those. Are you feeling better, Sarah?'

'Yes.' She tried to inject some lightness into her voice. 'I feel like a fraud for taking up a hospital bed.'

'Do whatever the doctors tell you. They know best. I'll see you tomorrow morning for sure. OK?'

'Yes, of course. Goodnight, Ben.'

There was a slight pause, then a sigh. 'Goodnight, Sarah.'

She put the telephone down, wondering if he was remembering how hungrily they had kissed the night before. Whether he felt the same desire now . . . as she did. But he hadn't come, she reminded herself despondently, and if they stayed away from each other . . .

'He's not coming to visit you, is he?' Angela commented cuttingly.

'Tomorrow, he said,' Sarah answered, unable to keep the disappointment out of her voice.

'I tell you, Sarah, you can't count on Ben. He's unreliable. He only thinks about what he wants to do. You'll be better off not marrying him.'

Sarah noted the ring of self-justification in Angela's tone but she could not ignore the fact that Ben's sister had a lifetime of knowing him. 'You're probably right,' she muttered.

There was an uncomfortable silence while they both contemplated the situation, then Sarah couldn't bear her friend's company any longer. 'Angela, if you don't mind, I'm—I'm rather tired.'

'I'll go.' Angela stood up abruptly but she hesitated, her expression clouded with uncertainty. 'I'm sorry I ever opened my mouth. About anything. I'll keep right out of your affairs from now on, Sarah. I promise.'

Sarah forced a smile. 'I know you meant well, Angela. Thanks for coming and bringing my stuff.'

Angela's smile was a twist of self-mockery. 'The good Samaritan who needs her tongue cut out. With my experience of crime reporting I should know better.'

'You did what you thought was best,' Sarah said in exoneration.

'That's what they say about murdered do-gooders,' Angela wisecracked on her way out the door.

But she had done some good, Sarah eventually acknowledged as she reviewed the events of the last few days. Angela had forced her into looking at the situation from a more objective perspective, and the longer Sarah considered her position, the more unreal and untenable it became.

Too much had happened too quickly. She wasn't sure where she was. Ben hadn't come to see her and had given no explanation for his absence. Angela was probably right. He was feckless and capricious, acting on impulse without any continuity of purpose. And Sarah suddenly realised that she was relying on him. She still felt hurt and disappointed that he hadn't turned up to be with her. Hadn't she learnt the lesson with Julian that the only person she could rely on was herself?

As for Julian, well, at least she had *that* problem sorted out as far as she was concerned. She didn't love him or want him. But he could become a very real thorn in Ben's side if he thought Sarah was marrying Angela's brother just for the money she would save him. If Julian kept up his pursuit of her she would have to make a very firm stand about her marriage to Ben.

The problem was, Sarah was no longer sure what that stand would be. She had never felt so compellingly attracted to a man, and it wasn't just physical. She liked everything about Ben: the way he talked to her and listened, his kindness and consideration of her feelings, his respect for her ideas and aims in life. But maybe that manner came easily to him because he hadn't had to sustain it for long. A weekend was hardly any test.

If he truly was as unreliable as Angela claimed, then he would show his true colours soon enough. After all, she didn't have to marry him. The taxation problem was Ben's, not hers. She had told him she needed time. It was his decision to stay with her rather than pursue a more certain course of resolving his problem. She wouldn't try to hold him if he wanted to back off from the marriage concept of family life. She wasn't at all sure he wasn't already backing off. Obviously they both needed time to be sure that they weren't making a terrible mistake.

Meanwhile she had to get her life back into order and that centred on her job. She had to get back to work tomorrow. It wasn't as if she were really sick, and God knew what Frances Chatfield might get up to if she stayed away any longer. After the scene on Saturday morning, Sarah had no doubt that Frances would do her spiteful best to undermine her authority in the Young Trends department even further.

Having settled on these decisive courses of action, Sarah slept quite well that night, but the next morning she ran into an unexpected difficulty. The day sister informed her that she could not leave the hospital until a doctor signed her out.

'But you can't keep me a prisoner here,' Sarah protested.

'If you go without the proper authority, the police will bring you back,' the sister stated, as immovable as a brick wall on rules and regulations.

'But I'm not sick. The doctor saw me this morning. Why didn't he sign my release?' Sarah demanded in frustration.

'Fear of a cerebral haemorrhage,' came the clipped reply.

Which gave Sarah pause for thought. 'Is there any real risk of that?' she asked uncertainly.

The sister shrugged. 'Slight. But no doctor or hospital wants to risk being sued for not taking proper care.'

Looking after their own interests more than hers. Sarah decided irritably. She didn't even have a headache. It was ridiculous that she had to stay here when she was perfectly well. 'Can't I write some statement releasing everyone from being responsible for my health?' she demanded.

The day sister's face set into sour disapproval. 'There is a form you can sign if that is your wish, but I strongly advise against it.'

But the need for positive action was too strong for Sarah to heed the advice. She wanted to get moving and move she did. However, by the time she had fulfilled the necessary formalities and got dressed it was already past nine o'clock. She would be hideously late for work, but better late than let Frances Chatfield have another day to work her poison, Sarah firmly reasoned.

Fortunately she had enough money in her handbag to pay the taxi fare into the city. Despite the small fortune it would cost her, she didn't feel she could afford to wait for a slow train from Penrith. Nor did she feel there was any point in waiting for Ben to turn up. He hadn't turned up last night. He could easily catch up with her . . . if he wanted to.

While she waited for the taxi to arrive Sarah was

called back to the reception desk. Her heart gave a delighted skip when one of the clerks directed her to a telephone, but when she lifted the receiver it was not Ben's voice that greeted her, but Julian's.

'How are you, Sarah?' he asked on a note of concern.

'I'm fine, thank you, Julian,' she answered politely.

'I went to the apartment to see you last night, but no one was at home, and I didn't find out about your accident until this morning. We must talk, Sarah. This can't go on.'

Sarah immediately bridled at his dictatorial tone. 'Julian, I've just checked out of the hospital and I'm waiting for a taxi to take me to work. It'll turn up any minute now. I'm sorry, but talking is not going to make any difference to how I feel. Thank you for calling, but ...'

'I'll see you tonight,' he said determinedly.

Sarah heaved a sigh of frustration. 'Julian, please don't do that. It's over.'

'I've been talking to Angela. I know all about her brother.'

Sarah could hear the resentment in his voice and tried to set him straight. 'Whatever Angela told you has nothing to do with us. Please, just let it go, Julian.'

'I suppose you had a great laugh at my expense.'

Her heart sank. 'No. I'm sorry you see it that

way. I was only trying to——'

'Taxi for Miss Woodley!'

She waved at the cabbie whose head was poked enquiringly round the reception door. 'I'm sorry, Julian. I have to go now. My taxi's here and I'm late for work as it is.'

'That's right! Put your job ahead of——'

She hung up. She knew it was rude. She angrily hoped it was unforgivable. There simply wasn't any point in going round and round the same futile arguments.

As she hurried out to the taxi Sarah was surprised to find that she was not quite as well as she had thought. Her knees had a disconcerting tendency to turn quite jelly-like, and her head spun a little at any sharp movement. It was probably the effect of having lain in bed too long, she decided, but was glad she had called a taxi. She could relax and rest all the way to the door of the department store.

Despite her good intentions, Sarah could not relax during the trip. She fretted over not having got the Penny Walker contract. Something had to be done. She couldn't just let it go. She alighted from the taxi, imbued with a sense of purpose, but as soon as she entered the store, Sarah knew something was wrong.

She was on friendly terms with most of her fellow workers, but there was an uneasiness in their reaction to her greetings. Was it the unusual lateness of her arrival that made them look shifty, Sarah wondered, or had the scene on Saturday morning plus her absence yesterday generated rumours that suggested a cautious manner might be wise? Store politics could be very tricky at times.

Sarah was not left in doubt for very long—only as long as it took her to reach the Young Trends department. The jolt was so comprehensive she stood rooted to the spot in sheer disbelief. All her displays had been changed! The whole upmarket thrust of the department had been diluted to the point that it had no visual impact at all.

For a few shaky moments Sarah thought she was going to faint. It was the shock of seeing all her work undone, on top of the residual shock of the accident, she reasoned sternly, in a desperate attempt to pull herself together. She couldn't appear weak now. Her sales assistants had noted her arrival and were watching her, waiting warily for her reaction.

Sarah beckoned over Ashley Thompson, who shared Sarah's own enthusiasm for innovative fashions. 'Who organised this abomination, Ashley?'

'Mrs Chatfield.'

It could have been no one else, Sarah knew, but it was as well to have absolute confirmation.

'I'm sorry, Sarah, but there was nothing we

could do about it,' Ashley explained in anxious sympathy.

'Not your responsibility,' Sarah nodded and handed over her handbag and overnight bag. 'Take care of these for me, will you? I'm about to do battle.'

'Sarah, be carful,' Ashley warned. 'She's out to get you.'

Sarah conjured up a reassuring smile. 'Well, I'm not got yet! I'll take this showdown right to the top and no way will I back down this time. Wish me luck, Ashley.'

Her speech won a relieved grin from the girl. 'You can call on our support if you think it'll do any good.'

'Thanks,' Sarah said gratefully, 'but this is strictly executive business and I aim to keep it on that level. It's best for you and the others to keep your noses clean. A job is a job, Ashley.'

'What about you?'

'I do not wish to work under Frances Chatfield's thumb,' Sarah declared decisively and, as she strode off with all the grim purpose of a determined combatant, she added, 'And I will not.'

She felt the same seething fury that she had felt with Julian last Friday. She had not been prepared to live under his thumb, either. If she was forced to break with the store she would, and to hell with the consequences. For years she had been diplomatic and tactful. For years she had struggled to build her department into what it was. She was not going to stand back and allow Frances Chatfield to negate all of that in just one day.

CHAPTER EIGHT

SARAH swept through the Ladies' Fashion department, her gaze flicking from side to side in single-minded search for Frances Chatfield. The sight of Julian conversing amicably with her antagonist came as another body blow. Sarah's stomach knotted. Her head whirled with possible implications, but whatever this double confrontation might mean there was no way she either could or would avoid it now.

Sarah barely hesitated in her step. Pride and determined aggression lifted her chin. She marched towards them without any outward display of concern, but the blood was pounding through her ears like a martial drum calling her to battle.

Somehow they sensed her approach before she reached them. Both heads swung towards her simultaneously. Mutual satisfaction was stamped on their faces. As they turned to face her, Sarah noted the glint of smug triumph in Frances Chatfield's eyes.

Julian took a step forward, holding out his hand to Sarah. 'Mrs Chatfield has just been telling me of the latest reorganisation. The end result will . . .'

'This is not your business, Julian,' Sarah cut in swiftly. 'It's mine!' She focused her attention entirely on the woman at his side. 'Good morning, Frances.' It was the first time she had ever called the older woman by her first name, deliberately denying her superior status.

Frances Chatfield's eyes hardened. A disdainful smile curled her lips. 'You're very late, Sarah. What is your excuse?'

The silky condescension of her tone barely sheathed the smug snipe in the words. Sarah grimly controlled the bristling hostility that surged through her and spoke with measured calmness. 'If I need an excuse, Frances, I'll be giving it to Howard Bowman directly, not to you.'

The smile took on a superior tilt. 'On the contrary, you will report to me, my dear. I promised Howard I'd eradicate this malingering, and he has given me the responsibility of handling all such conflicts with company interests on this floor.'

Not by a flicker of an eyelid did Sarah betray her inner dismay. 'I don't believe you,' she said flatly.

The smile moved into a full-blown sneer. 'Then you're in for a shock, aren't you? After the conference on Friday, and what happened on Saturday morning, it was decided you might be a trifle . . . unreliable.' She rolled out the word with rich relish, pausing over it for maximum effect before continuing. 'Your non-attendance at work yesterday tended to confirm that opinion. Young Trends is being given back to me as part of my responsibilities.'

'And you took it upon yourself to change my displays,' Sarah bit out in barely contained fury.

'Of course. Since I'll be accountable for——'

The fury exploded. 'You're a fool, Frances! It's my department until Howard Bowman tells me otherwise. If what you say is true, then you'd better get him down here straight away, because I'm going back to Young Trends right now to remove that incredibly insipid choice of clothes. And I will not tolerate your interference, so don't try it. Don't ever try to interfere with me again.'

She had swung on her heel and was off before Frances could open her mouth. A hand caught her shoulder. She shrugged it off and whirled with one hand already raised to ward off any further detention, but it was Julian who had hurried after her.

'This is another reckless decision, Sarah. Can't you see what a fool you'll make of yourself? Which is precisely what you've been doing ever since last Friday,' he added with pointed resentment. 'If you'll only listen to me!'

'I listened to you for too long,' she snapped, impatient with his self-serving interference.

'Dammit, Sarah! Can't you see? You've even failed at this job that's so important to you. Don't fight it. Let Frances do it. You're well out of it.'

'I didn't ask for your opinion, Julian, nor do I want it,' she retorted fiercely.

She swung away from him, but again he caught her back. 'I want us to get back together, Sarah. I know all about Ben Haviland. You can't use him as a red herring any more, so ——'

'A red herring!' Sarah scorned. 'You don't know anything, Julian! Now take your hands off me because I have other more important things to attend to.'

She marched off but he trailed in her wake, riled into retaliation. 'Finished, are we? It'll be you and Haviland who'll be finished if you take up with him. I promise you that. I'll break him if it's the last thing I do. He won't get away from me as easily as he did from Frances.'

Sarah paused and rounded on him. 'Don't tangle with Ben, Julian. He's a lot bigger than you. In every way,' she added scathingly, then wished she had held her tongue.

Julian's eyes narrowed. 'You'd take him just for his money, wouldn't you?'

'No!' She was appalled at having led him to think any such thing. It suddenly hit her that not once had she been really tactful or kind to Julian over ending their long relationship. For the most part, she had simply reacted against his arrogant selfishness. She owed him more consideration than that. They had shared a lot of happy times together and it was wrong to end it all with such bitter hostility. With a softer voice and an apologetic expression she tried to mitigate the hurt she had given him.

'I'm sorry, Julian. The decision I made on Friday must have come as a shock to you. I was upset by various things at the time and I didn't behave well, but it wasn't a reckless decision. I've had doubts about how our marriage would work out ever since we became engaged. It was a mistake on my part, and I apologise very sincerely for it. I was trying too hard to be the kind of woman you wanted. But I'm not that kind of woman, Julian, and——'

'I can see that,' he cut in bitterly.

Sarah took a deep breath. 'Then you can see it wouldn't have worked between us,' she finished, determinedly maintaining a soft tone. 'Please excuse me now. There can't be any good purpose served over our aguing any further. I hope you will find someone else who'll suit you better.'

'Like you found Ben Haviland,' Julian sneered at her.

Sarah stared back at him for several seconds, realising that the damage done was irrevocable and there was nothing she could now do or say to appease Julian. She turned away and hurried towards Young Trends, not glancing back, hoping against hope that Julian would just give up and go away. She hadn't handled the break-up well. In fact she was now ashamed of the hostility she had displayed. No matter what the provocation, she should have given Julian more leeway for a dignified exit from her life.

But there was no time for self-castigation now. She had to take positive steps to counteract Frances Chatfield's sly manoeuvring. If the older woman really did have Howard Bowman's support, then Sarah would very shortly be confronting the managing director himself, and she intended to have some ammunition of her own ready.

'I want the clothes we had on this central display as fast as you can find them,' she told Ashley Thompson who was instantly alert to Sarah's return.

'Only be a minute,' Ashley replied eagerly.

Sarah began to undress the models.

'I'm beginning to think you're right about finishing our relationship, Sarah,' Julian's voice said behind her. 'Only a fool would go against Frances, and I don't want to be associated with a fool.'

'Then why don't you go?' she suggested coldly, not pausing in her work even to glance at him.

'Because I want to watch you get your come-uppance.'

Sarah swallowed down the sour bile that almost gorged her throat. It had been Julian himself who had triggered this conflict with his telephone call on Friday, and she was the one paying for his self-indulgence. It took every ounce of control she had not to turn around and stick him with the pins she had gathered in her hand. Ashley Thompson's return with the fashion outfits she wanted was a very timely distraction.

With Ashley's help, Sarah managed to reclothe the models before Frances arrived with Howard Bowman in tow. Sarah took up her stand right next to the display and greeted the managing director with every outward show of confidence, aware that Julian, as well as her assistants, were hovering in the background. She went straight into the attack, refusing him the opportunity to suggest a change of venue for a more private discussion.

'Mr Bowman, I do not appreciate having my department sabotaged by a person who has no understanding whatsoever of what young people want in fashion today.'

'Sabotage is a strong word, Sarah. You should have come to me when you arrived this morning and I would have explained the situation to you,' he replied in an appeasing tone.

'I told Sarah to see you, Howard,' Frances

Chatfield declared primly. 'Her insubordination cannot be tolerated.'

Howard Bowman frowned at Frances, then attempted to project concern at Sarah. 'The fact of the matter is, we have given your position a lot of thought, Sarah. Obviously you are not really a career person. Frances is. And in the long term we think it better if she is responsible——'

'Responsible for what, Mr Bowman?' Sarah cut in scathingly. 'Responsible for watering down this department to an insipid reflection of her own? Just take a good, considered look around you. Every display on this floor, bar this one, is Frances Chatfield's idea of what the young should be buying. But the young, Mr Bowman, have not yet joined the twin-set brigade. Their tastes and wants are different. A whole generation different!' She took a deep breath and added forcefully, 'Which department is making more money?'

His frown deepened as he cast his eye around. 'Well, I . . . er . . . really think we should talk about this in private.'

Sarah was determined not to budge. 'The figures tell their own story, Mr. Bowman. You know that for the floor area covered I've run the most profitable department in the clothing field. I've got the results on the books, and I think it's about time that the executive board appreciated those figures. In fact, I meant to raise the Penny Walker contract again this morning, because this store is going to lose very badly if we don't tie up a deal with her. You only get such a golden opportunity once.'

Howard Bowman looked even more uncomfortable. He glanced worriedly at Frances Chatfield, who sensed her advantage slipping. 'You know what the decision was on Friday, Howard,' she reminded him waspishly. 'And if you don't back me up now, I'll report everything that has happened to the chairman.'

'The chairman wasn't impressed with you on Friday, Sarah,' Howard agreed ponderously. 'And of course your unexplained absence yesterday . . .'

'She should be fired,' Frances shot in malevolently. 'It's her or me, Howard. You've got ample proof of how unreliable she is. And you can see how insolently she is treating me now.'

The effort already expended on her defence had made Sarah feel dizzy. She clutched at her head in an attempt to keep it steady enough to continue the fight. 'My absence yesterday——'

'Sarah!'

The loud, urgent cry startled them all, and they turned towards it. Ben Haviland was charging across the department floor, and the sight of him brought such a surge of relief to Sarah that her knees wobbled. He had said he would come to her today and he had kept his word.

'Ben?' she breathed hopefully, her hand instinctively reaching out to him.

He swept her up in this arms, cradling her with tender care as he anxiously scaned her face. 'Don't ever do that to me again!' he commanded. 'You've had me worried crazy. When Penny and I got to the hospital and you weren't there . . .'

'Penny?' Sarah asked a little dazedly. It was wonderful to have Ben's arms around her again, and he cared about her. He really did care. But what was he doing with her favourite dress-designer?

'I brought her along to talk business with you. But you'd left. You shouldn't be here, Sarah. The doctors warned me you could have a cerebral haemorrhage. What are you thinking of, taking such a risk with our future?'

Our future. What beautiful words they were, Sarah thought happily.

'You're coming home with me right now,' continued Ben. 'And no argument. I'm going to make sure you take proper care of yourself, even if I have to stand over you every minute of the day and night.'

'What on earth is going on?' Howard Bowman blustered. 'What hospital? And what's all this about a cerebral haemorrhage?'

Ben glowered at him. 'Who are you?'

'I'm the managing director of this store.'

'Then you ought to be horse-whipped for letting Sarah come back to work.'

Howard instantly took umbrage. 'Kindly explain that statement. I'll have you know——'

'What do you run here? A slave-factory?' Ben cut in contemptuously. 'The car accident on Sunday wasn't Sarah's fault, and if you . . .'

'I wasn't told anything about a car accident!'

Ben glared accusingly at Frances Chatfield. 'Angela telephoned you. You knew Sarah was suffering from concussion. I suppose you wanted her dead too, just like poor old Tramp.'

'How dare you!' Frances spluttered.

'I think you'd better explain yourself, Frances,' Howard Bowman said curtly. 'You gave me to understand that Sarah . . .'

'Don't believe a word Frances tells you. She's a liar!' Ben spat in disgust.

'And you're a fraud, Haviland!' Julian stepped from the sidelines and placed himself at Frances Chatfield's side, his expression one of triumphant malevolence. 'I know all about your tax avoidance scheme and I'm going to take you to the cleaners,' he gloated.

'No!' Sarah cried, so alarmed on Ben's behalf that she struggled against the warm security of his embrace. 'You have to let me go, Ben. I know how much you hate pressures. I can't marry you if it's going to ruin you.'

He smiled and clutched her more tightly. 'Don't you worry about a thing, Sarah. He can't touch us.'

'Oh, yes, I can,' Julian sniped. 'I've got the evidence of your sister that any marriage you enter into is completely bogus, just to split your income.'

'Angela!' Ben said in surprise, then laughed out loud. 'Good God, man! Angela's the greatest practical joker in the world. If she said that, she was pulling your leg. And you fell for it!'

'She was serious!' Julian insisted fiercely. 'And that's avoidence, Haviland. A bogus marriage won't wash with the tax department. I'll get you on Section 260A.'

'And I'll back him up.' Frances hurled in. 'I'll bear witness to what an artful dodger you are, Ben Haviland. You promised to marry me once, and——'

'You're right, Frances,' Ben agreed, his face suddenly puckering in concern. 'That was a terrible thing I did to you and I'm sorry. It was very wrong, running away like that. Cowardly. I've only just started to grow up and appreciate how badly I treated you, and I'm deeply ashamed that I didn't handle the differences between us in a more kindly and considerate way. I don't expect you to forgive me . . .'

'No, I won't!' she shot at him, not the least bit mollified by his apology.

'And neither will I for what you've done to Sarah,' Julian sniped.

'I'm sorry. I'm sorry for both of you,' Ben said in

another attempt at appeasement. 'But I can't change what's happened. Sarah and I love each other, and ...'

Julian gave a mocking laugh. 'That's impossible! You've barely met.'

'It's true, none-the-less,' Ben stated seriously. 'Now, if you'll excuse us, I'm taking Sarah home. She's not well and shouldn't be here.'

'Now just a minute——' Howard Bowman began.

But Ben didn't let him finish. 'You've had your chance. You should have seen Sarah's worth and promoted her. I'm going to put her in her own boutique. Let her run it as she sees fit.' He turned back to Julian with a last word of well-meant advice. 'And as for trying to prove a bogus marriage, you'll find yourself a laughing stock when Sarah's expecting our first baby.'

Julian glared at Sarah. 'You gold-digging bitch! You've slept with him already!'

'If I wasn't holding Sarah, you'd pay for that,' Ben growled at him. 'You'd better keep out of Sarah's way in future, or so help me God, I'll drop you from the tallest building I can find. Without benefit of clergy or parachute!'

And with that he started to stride off, carrying Sarah like a precious prize that he'd never let go. Sarah's mind registered a slightly out-of-focus picture: Julian, an alien figure of furious frustration, Frances, the scrupulously put-together fashion-plate with her polished veneer cracking at the seams, Howard Bowman, affronted dignity stamped all over his posture, and behind them the display that Sarah had changed to reflect all that she herself had stood for. And Ben was carrying her away, away from the past and into their future, she thought with a mild sense of hysteria.

'Ben, I've got to get my bags,' she protested, even as she wound her arms around his neck in heartfelt gratitude for his wonderful support.

'Angela can get them later. We're going home, where you'll be safe from people like that.'

She snuggled her head on to his broad shoulder and wondered why she was accepting it all so passively. She had broken up with Julian over her job, fought with Frances to keep it, confronted the managing director himself, but she didn't mind at all that Ben had swept the whole thing aside. Either she really had gone weak in the head or . . . No, it was because he had proved he really cared about her. He had stood up to all three of her antagonists and fought them for her sake. Master of the situation, she thought with blissful pride, even against Frances.

They had to wait for an elevator and Ben's mouth brushed warmly over her hair. 'Sarah, are you feeling bad?' he asked anxiously.

'Not now you're here,' she murmured contentedly.

The doors opened and he carried her into the small compartment where they were entirely alone. Ben held her a little more tightly and Sarah didn't feel the least bit suffocated by his closeness. She felt wonderfully cherished.

'Why did you come back here?' Ben asked, his voice vibrating with concern. 'I thought you were safe at the hospital.'

'I was worried about my job, and I thought . . . I thought *you* might have had second thoughts, Ben.'

'I told you I'd come to the hospital today,' he reminded her chidingly.

Sarah heaved a regretful sigh that she hadn't waited for him. 'Well, you didn't come last night, and Angela said that maybe I shouldn't rely on you. I'm sorry, Ben, but things have been happening so fast, I just wasn't sure.'

'Angela's getting to be a damned busybody,' he muttered grimly.

The elevator doors opened on the ground floor and Ben strode out again, making for the Pitt Street exit. 'Penny's got a taxi waiting for us. I took her to the hospital with me to discuss the boutique with you, but when you were missing . . .' He dragged in a sharp breath. 'I know I said you could come and go as you please, Sarah, but next time, would you tell me first? It did terrible things to my stomach, not knowing where you were.'

'Same thing for me, Ben,' she said in soft appeal. 'It did terrible things to my stomach last night, not knowing what you were doing. Or thinking.'

He frowned, obviously giving the matter deep thought as he continued out to the pavement where the taxi was waiting for them.

Penny Walker jumped out of the back seat, her fresh young face a picture of relief. 'You found her!' she cried.

'Penny, I think we'd better leave our business until tomorrow,' Ben said quickly. 'Would you mind?'

'Of course not. Give me a call when Sarah feels up to it. You take the taxi and I'll find my own way home.'

'Thanks, Penny,' he accepted gratefully, and bundled Sarah into the taxi without pause, giving the driver their home address even as he waved goodbye to Penny.

Sarah laid her head back against the seat, feeling rather drained by all the morning's emotional activity. Ben wrapped his hand around hers in a warmly possessive way. He did not relax, and for a few moments his uneasiness unsettled her, until he spoke.

'Sarah, I'm sorry about worrying you yesterday. I didn't tell you what I was planning because I wasn't sure how much I could do, but once I met

Penny things got rolling pretty fast and I was so anxious to get you out of that store. I know how much you like being in the fashion busines, but I couldn't stand the thought of you going back to work with that poisonous woman.'

The warm surge of happiness pulsed from Sarah's heart. 'You were thinking of me?'

Ben's mouth curved in bemusement. 'I can't think of anything else. I thought if I could get your boutique set up before you got out of hospital, you'd be happy to give up your job at the store.' His eyes appealed for forgiveness. 'I guess I shouldn't have said you were resigning, but when I looked at Frances, I couldn't bear you to be even near her any more. But I shouldn't have pushed what I wanted on to you. If you want to go back . . .?'

'No.' She smiled her pleasure in him. 'I thought you were marvellous, the way you stood up to Frances and told her off.'

He sighed in relief. 'I'd do anything for you, Sarah. And I wanted to come to you last night, but I had this sense of urgency over setting you up in the business you wanted, and Penny organised a meeting with these other young designers she reckons are good. I figured if Penny thought so you would, too. And they'd all be happy to stock your boutique, Sarah. All you've got to do is give them a deadline. And I've got a list of shops for lease that you can choose from . . .'

He stopped as Sarah started to laugh. 'Oh, Ben!' she gasped. 'You've got me on that roller-coaster again!'

He looked perplexed. 'What roller-coaster?'

'The one you've had me riding on ever since we met.'

He frowned. 'Am I going too fast for you, Sarah?'

'I do feel a little dizzy,' she confessed.

'I'm talking too much. You just rest. I've got to take care of you,' he said in quick concern, then settled back, determinedly silent, although his hand fondled hers with a persistent sense of possessiveness.

Sarah marvelled at all he had done for her. What other man who had no first-hand experience of the fashion world would have plunged into it as Ben had, just to protect her and please her? What other man had ever really listened to her ideas and taken appreciative note of them? Or made her feel so cared for? And the most wonderful part was, she knew with absolute certainty, that it wasn't all a false front to coax her into marriage. Ben was no actor. What you saw was what you got. And he really was marvellous.

When the taxi pulled up at their apartment block at Neutral Bay, Ben was out like a flash and round at her door before Sarah had even moved. He handed the driver the fare, then scooped Sarah up into his arms again.

'I can walk, Ben,' she demurred weakly.

'Not if you're dizzy. I'm going to put you straight to bed, Sarah. No more risks today,' he insisted.

She wasn't really dizzy. Not physically dizzy. It was only her emotions that were spinning like crazy, but Sarah didn't correct Ben. She hung on to him, secretly revelling in his strength and tenderness, and when he ultimately carried her into her bedroom and gently laid her on the bed, she did not want to unlock her arms from around his neck. His mouth was close to her own, and the sensual curve of his lips reminded her very forcefully of what even their lightest touch could do to her.

'Thank you for everything, Ben,' she whispered.

'Sarah ...' Her name was a strained breath of need, mingling with hers.

The temptation was too great to resist. Even as she pulled his head down to hers, it flashed through her mind that she was inviting trouble. But it seemed so long since he had last kissed her, and right now, she needed that more than anything else in the world. The urgent, searching pressure of his lips against her own took Sarah's breath away. Little shivers of excitement ran down her spine. She could not stop her hands from sliding over his strongly muscled back, pressing him closer to her, wanting the deepening of his kiss, wanting ...

Ben suddenly broke away, the separation so abrupt that Sarah was stunned by a sharp sense of bereftness. She stared up at him, eyes glazed with unsatisfied passion. His chest was heaving as he dragged in gasping breaths. He groaned and gathered her up to him in a crushing embrace, his cheek rubbing against hers in an agony of longing.

'I need you, Sarah. I want you so much I'm going insane thinking about you all the time. I can't control it and I don't even want to control it. I don't even care about the money anymore. Only you. Only you.'

His fingers threaded through her hair and gently tugged her head back. His eyes glittered feverishly, desire fighting with an intensity of purpose that begged her understanding. 'I'm not going to rush you, Sarah. I'll wait for ever for you. I want you to be sure. I couldn't bear it if you weren't happy with me.'

'But——'

'No, listen to me!' he pleaded, with so much pent-up feeling that Sarah held her tongue. 'I'll pay whatever is necessary, and I'll wait for you as long as it takes because I don't want to live without you. We'll do whatever you want, I promise you. And I'll try to be everything you want.'

'Oh, Ben! You are. You are everything I want,' Sarah cried, knowing in that moment that she had never spoken a greater truth. And she kissed him with all the exultant conviction in her heart and soul.

She felt the shudder of passion run through Ben's body as he bore her back down to the pillow and followed her, his heavy, powerful legs covering hers, his broad, muscular chest almost flattening the soft fullness of her breasts. But she didn't care. She hugged him even closer, glorying in the hard, male strength of him, responding fiercely to the wild hunger of his mouth and the feverish caress of his hands.

His legs entwined with hers, holding her to him as he shifted on to his side. His hand closed over her breast, softly kneading it into swelling sensitivity. He rained kisses over her face, gasping incoherent words of need and want, and Sarah surrendered to it all with a savage joy that rampaged through her veins and melted all her bones.

She cried an instinctive protest when Ben made to pull away from her. He groaned as he resisted the frantic clutch of her hands. 'Sarah ... Sarah ...' Harsh agonised bursts of breath. 'I shouldn't be doing this. The excitement ... it might kill you.'

A great welling of love pumped from her heart. 'It's strong medicine, Ben,' she whispered, then more urgently, 'I need you. I need you.'

'Oh, God!' he moaned, and restraint was flung to the winds.

Sarah felt no embarrassment, no twinge of

shame as Ben undressed her, and when he undressed himself, the revelation of his magnificent body sent quivers of excitement through her. For the first time in her life she felt a glorious sense of rightness in this intimate sharing of nakedness: man and woman ... as they were made for each other ... to touch, to hold, to join, to be as one.

She welcomed him with all that she was, answering the urgency of his need with an explosion of passion that exulted in every touch, every movement, every pressure. And nothing, nothing in the whole of creation, could have been more right than their possession of each other, their bodies driving together in an ecstatic fusion that shattered every barrier of self and tipped them into another incredible dimension of feeling where neither could exist without the other.

They lay together for a long time, blissfully content, lightly touching in soft wonderment as they thought their own thoughts. If she had really had any doubts about falling in love with Ben Haviland, they had all been put behind her now. Sarah knew he was her man for the rest of her life. Never had she known such completeness, such utter fulfilment as a woman. How could there be anyone else like him?

She nestled closer, rubbing her cheek across his shoulder, kissing the pulse at the base of his throat. His arm came around her, holding her there, wanting her there. She smiled her contentment.

'Ben?' she murmured, reluctant to break the
beautiful harmony of their silence.

'Mmm?' It was a hum of blissful satisfaction.

Her smile gathered a happy indulgence. 'I think
we should get married straight away and save the
money.'

Ben's arm hugged her even closer. 'Nothing I'd
like better, but, Sarah, don't get me wrong now . . .
that thirtieth of June date doesn't apply any more.
It never really did. So if you want more time . . .'

She lifted her head in surprise. 'Never really
applied? You said it was terribly important and
urgent.'

'Only you are important, my love.' His fingers
played a delicately sensuous tune on her spine, and
his smile widened into a joyful grin. 'And urgent.
But the fact is that Julian will get his pound of
flesh, no matter what. Besides, as I said before, I
don't give a damn about the money as long as I have
you. I want you to name whatever date you like.'

Sarah stared at him. 'But if we can save all that
money by marrying straight away, then . . .'

'Sarah, please, forget the damned money!' He
sounded almost goaded, then added defiantly, 'The
tax thing never had anything to do with why I
asked you to marry me.'

'Never?' The word came out as an outraged
squawk as Sarah recalled all the worrying she had

done over his financial problems.

Ben's face screwed into a rueful appeal. 'I couldn't think of anything else fast enough and I had to get your mind off Julian. Give you something else to think about, so you wouldn't get depressed and want him back. I figured if I could get you to see me as husband material straight away, I'd have more chance with you. And since you were obviously a businesswoman, I thought the money angle might intrigue you.'

His eyes begged her understanding. 'It was a hell of a spot to be in, Sarah, meeting the woman you've been looking for all your life and finding her hung up on some other guy. I was desperate. I've never worked so hard, trying to give you all the right options and answers to get you concentrating on me. It was like threading through a minefield. But I never once lied to you about the kind of relationship we'll have, Sarah,' he added anxiously. 'I'd do anything in the world to ensure you stay happy with me.'

'Oh, Ben!' The sigh turned into a rueful smile. He was so irresistibly wonderful that she instantly forgave him all his schemes. 'I think you must be the most marvellous inventor in the whole world, and I don't care about anything else either. I still want us to get married straight away,' she insisted firmly, and saw in his eyes his blissful joy in her, the love that made everything else unimportant.

'Best thing,' he agreed happily. 'Do it as soon as we can!'

And in the kiss that sealed their agreement was the promise of the most positive future there could ever be for a man and a woman who had found their true mate in each other.

CHAPTER NINE

'HOLD on a minute! I can't believe this!' Angela threw up her hands, pushed herself out of the armchair, and started pacing the living-room floor, a worried frown creasing her brow.

'It's true,' Ben said, looking down at Sarah for support.

She was snuggled next to him on the sofa and she nodded her head in agreement. 'It just happened. There was nothing either of us could do about it. It's got nothing to do with Ben's original situation, Angela,' she assured her friend.

'Not even going to have a marriage contract,' Ben added for good measure. 'In fact, I shouldn't have even mentioned it. Don't know why I even thought of it. It got Sarah all confused and unhappy about marrying me. But we've got it all straightened out now. Everything's perfect, isn't it, Sarah?'

She smiled her love up at him and Ben beamed his right back at her.

Angela confronted her brother with mounting exasperation. 'Do you realise I've been working my butt off, cajoling, flattering, imploring and pleading in order to get someone to marry you? And now you're going to marry my best friend!'

'I did warn you,' Ben pointed out. 'It's your fault if you don't listen. I told you to cancel——'

'But at that time Sarah said she wasn't marrying you,' Angela argued.

'I never believed it!' Ben declared. 'You didn't mean it, did you, Sarah?'

'Well, I was a bit confused . . .'

'And rightly so. My fault,' Ben stated grandly, completely exonerating her from any blame whatsoever.

Sarah breathed a happy sigh. It was marvellous having Ben think she was perfect. Of course, there might come a time when he changed his mind about that, but Sarah firmly resolved to make him keep thinking it as long as it was humanly possible.

Angela stared down at them, still shaking her head. 'Well, I suppose I can cope with being made to look foolish. What I find most alarming is you two.'

Ben looked surprised. 'Nothing wrong with us, is there, Sarah?'

But Angela wasn't mollified. 'Now don't start that again!' she whipped out. 'For all your waywardness, Ben, you are my brother, and I love you for that reason if for no other. And Sarah is my best friend. I hate the thought of both of you making each other miserable for the rest of your lives because of some mistaken notion . . .'

'It's not a mistaken notion,' Ben cut in, affronted at the very idea. 'It was love at first sight. Didn't believe in it until it happened. But when I saw Sarah I said to myself, that's the woman I want and if I can't have her, I don't want any other.'

'And Ben certainly had a strong effect on me from the very first meeting,' Sarah insisted.

'You've got no idea what it's like, Angela.' Ben hit a fist into the palm of his other hand in illustration. 'Like being smacked over the head with a sledge-hammer.'

'Or being thrown out of the window on the fourth floor,' Sarah laughed, remembering her feeling of being on a runaway roller-coaster.

Angela still looked slightly sceptical. 'Are you two certain it's love and not just strong attraction?'

'Both!' said Ben, very positively. 'Of course we'll have our differences. We've had them already. But we're very good at sorting them out, aren't we, Sarah? And that's because we love each other, Angela. There's nothing I want more than Sarah to be happy with me, and no one can say or do anything that will ever change that.'

Angela looked a little dazed by this speech. She heaved a sigh and dropped back into her armchir. She lifted her hand in a helpless gesture as if to say it was all beyond her but she had done her best and what more could she do? 'Well, I suppose you want me to vacate the apartment,' she said vaguely.

'Of course not. I bought it for you, didn't I? I've never been an Indian giver, Angela,' Ben chided her.

Angela offered an apologetic grimace. 'Sorry. You've just knocked me for five. Or six. Or seven. I don't know what to think any more.'

'Sarah and I are going to buy a big house on a double block,' Ben announced. 'And then we're going to fill it with kids.'

'And two dogs,' Sarah added to complete the picture.

Ben grinned happily at her. 'Maybe more. Depends on what the kids want.'

Angela looked incredulously at Ben. 'Is this really my maverick brother?'

He shot her a serious look. 'Well, it's like this, Angela. Sarah showed me a whole new way of looking at things. I was missing out, you know. Didn't even see it until I met Sarah. I owe her an awful lot.'

Sarah squeezed his hand in blissful contentment. 'You showed me some good things too, Ben.'

His hand squeezed back. 'We were meant for each other, Sarah.'

'So, when's the wedding?' Angela asked, resigning herself to the inevitable.

'Twenty-fifth of June,' Ben answered promptly. 'And we've got to start getting organised.'

The doorbell rang and Angela looked suspiciously at Ben and Sarah as she rose to her feet. 'Is this another one of your surprises?' she demanded rhetorically, and opened the door with a theatrical flourish. 'I hope you don't want to marry Ben,' she tossed flippantly at the doorbell-ringer. 'Because he's already spoken for.'

'No, not at all,' came the startled reply. 'I work at the store with Sarah and she left her bags behind, so I thought . . .'

'Ashley!' Sarah jumped up to welcome her. 'Come on in.' She quickly introduced her to Angela and Ben and thanked her for her kindness in bringing the bags from the store. 'Have you time to stop a while? I guess I owe you and the other girls an apology for deserting the ship, so to speak.'

Ashley laughed as she dropped into an armchair. 'Actually we all felt like clapping. You sure socked it to them, Sarah. You and Ben,' she added, her eyes sparkling with admiration.

For the next half-hour Ashley regaled them with all the reactions of everyone at the store after Ben and Sarah had made their dramatic exit. Angela, having heard nothing of this morning's scene, kept prompting Ashley for every detail, and ended up rolling around the floor in helpless paroxysms of laughter.

'It wasn't all that funny,' Sarah chided her. 'In

fact, the situation before Ben arrived was really rather nasty.'

Ashley nodded agreement. 'It certainly was, and to tell you the truth, Sarah, I want to resign too, now that Mrs Chatfield's taking over. I was wondering if you'd consider me if you want a sales assistant when you open your boutique.'

Sarah looked at Ben and they both nodded together.

'Won't be until the end of July, Ashley,' Ben warned. 'Sarah reckons we should open the boutique with Penny Walker's spring collection and we need the time before then to get married, have a honeymoon and set up house.'

'But as soon as we're operational, we'll have you on the payroll,' Sarah assured her happily.

'That's fantastic!' Ashley was so excited she jumped up and kissed them both. 'And congratulations, too! I hope you'll both be very, very happy.'

And on Sarah's promise to keep in touch, Ashley took her leave. As soon as the door was closed behind her, Angela started raising more questions. 'What kind of wedding are you going to have? Register office?'

'No way!' said Ben decisively. 'We're having the full, proper ceremony. We've already broken the news to Sarah's parents and we're going up to Mount Victoria next weekend to get them organised.'

Angela's eyes widened at Sarah. 'How did your mum and dad take all this?'

'They thought it was a bit hasty at first, but we talked them around, didn't we, Ben?' She smiled up at him, and he chuckled in remembrance.

Angela took to shaking her head again. 'Well, if you're really having a proper wedding, you'll have to get Mum and Dad back from overseas. They certainly wouldn't want to miss this. They've been waiting for one or the other of us to marry for years.' She broke into a laugh. 'They sure didn't expect it to be you, Ben!'

'Will you be my bridesmaid, Angela?' Sarah asked eagerly.

'Love to.' Her eyes sparked with a wickedly teasing glint. 'I want all the inside information I can get. If you two end up murdering each other, it'll give me a crime scoop that'll knock my editor's eyes out.'

Ben laughed and hugged Sarah closer. 'Don't get your hopes up, Angela. That's never going to happen. But you can get one of your society reporters to cover the wedding. We've asked Penny Walker to design the dresses for the bridal party and it'll be a good bit of publicity for the boutique.'

Angela gave a bemused laugh. 'When you move, brother, you certainly do move!'

And that thought was to echo through Sarah's mind continually over the next few weeks. They moved at a hectic pace, having meetings with other young designers besides Penny Walker, choosing what Sarah wanted to sell and selecting just the right premises for the boutique. Ben scouted out houses for Sarah to look at and they eventually settled on a beautiful old home at Lane Cove because it had lovely big rooms and a huge garden. Then there was furniture to buy, fittings for her wedding dress, endless details to settle. Ben decided he would not replace the Ferrari with another sports car and turned up with two BMWs, saying they would be more practical for transporting babies and dogs.

After one particularly exhausting day, Sarah could not help remarking, 'For a man who can't stand the thought of having a job, you certainly work hard, Ben.'

He looked surprised. 'But this isn't work! We're creating something. That's a lot different to doing repetitive tasks. I love getting into something new and exciting.' He suddenly eyed her with anxious concern. 'I hope you don't mind my not having a regular job, Sarah, but I'd die if I wasn't doing something creative. Can you really put up with me?'

'I love you just as you are, Ben Haviland. I don't ever want you to change and don't you ever doubt that,' she assured him without the slightest hesitation.

He smiled in relief. 'You know one of the things I love about you, Sarah? You're such a positive person. And I've been thinking about a name for the boutique, something that expresses the whole concept you're after. How about The Positive Approach?'

'That's great!' Sarah threw her arms around his neck in enthusiastic fervour. 'You're a genius, Ben! An absolute genius!'

He laughed. 'If I am, it's you who inspires me.' And he kissed her in such an inspirational way that any kind of work was forgotten for quite some time.

Ben's parents flew home from Europe, absolutely thrilled about their son's marriage plans and delighted to meet Sarah and her family. In fact, Sarah got the distinct impression that they viewed her as some kind of miracle worker, which was a little unsettling. Occasionally she worried if Ben really would be happy with the family life they had planned, but then she would look at him and the doubts and fears melted away. Whatever happened in their future, she couldn't want any man other than Ben.

The wedding was a wonderfully happy occasion. Penny Walker had designed Sarah a magnificent dress in white silk taffeta with an appliquéd motif of pink and silver roses. Angela's deep pink bridesmaid's dress was the perfect complement. Ben was resplendent in silver-grey tails and one of

Sarah's brothers stood in as best man. Angela had not only organised a photographer from her newspaper, but also a friend to video the whole event 'so she could really believe it had actually happened'.

Jack Woodley declared that Ben was just the kind of son-in-law he had hoped to welcome into the family. Ben's father declared that Sarah was a girl in a million, several million in fact, and both mothers wept happy, sentimental tears when Ben and Sarah finally took their leave.

Ben had chosen the Bahamas for their honeymoon, and they spent a blissful three weeks cruising around the Caribbean. Everything was perfect—the weather, the balmy atmosphere of the islands, the tropical splendour around them, and, most of all, the marvellous intimacy of every touch, the instant understanding of every word, every expression of love that they shared.

'We'll have to go home some time,' Sarah said one morning.

'Mmm ... this year or next?' Ben murmured, stroking featherlight fingertips down her spine.

Sarah squirmed with pleasure. 'I'm getting fat and lazy, just lying around doing nothing.'

'You're beautiful, and you're not doing nothing,' Ben breathed huskily as he rolled her over into his arms.

And Sarah forgot to raise the matter again for

over a week. However, a letter from Ashley
Thompson and Penny Walker reminded her of her
responsibilities, and she felt quite burdened over
disturbing Ben about the scheduled opening of the
boutique. She was quite sure he had no real interest
in ladies' fashions and he had only involved himself
because it interested her. At this particular stage,
Sarah wondered why she had been so interested
herself, but took herself to task for the thought. It
would be positively delinquent of her not to fulfil
the obligations she had taken on.

Nevertheless, it was with some diffidence that
she approached the subject of going home once
again. To her surprise Ben agreed instantly, with
only one proviso. 'We must stop off in New York
on the way.'

'What do you want to do in New York?' Sarah
asked, uncaring about what they did as long as it
was together. 'Have you got business there?'

'I've been thinking ... We should put in some
spadework, Sarah. Got to plan for the future. I
know you'll get a lot of pleasure from running your
boutique because it's what you've dreamed of, and
it's always great for dreams to come true. I know
you've got the talent to do it well, but you're like
me, Sarah. You'll get bored doing repetitive stuff.
What you're really good at is spotting new
possibilities in fashion and we should prepare the
ground for you becoming an agent and expanding

overseas. New York's the place to start.'

'But how? What do I do?' Sarah spluttered, totally stunned by such an idea.

Ben grinned at her. 'The world is just one big market-place. You can take New York, London, even Paris by storm if you've got a mind to. You don't have to, but let's start making an opportunity in case you do want it. We'll drop in on some old friends in New York and set up some contacts. You could become the outstanding agent for new Australian designers and show their designs to the world. Pick the best. Quite exciting really, finding real originals.'

'Oh, Ben! What a fantastic idea!' Sarah breathed, her eyes shining with delight.

He laughed and swung her up in his arms. 'Thought you'd like it.'

'You've done so much for me, Ben. I wish there was something I could do for you.'

He kissed her. 'You're doing everything for me, all the time, just by being you and being with me,' he said with absolute conviction, and Sarah hoped with all her heart that that would be enough for him in all the years ahead.

CHAPTER TEN

THE London collection had been a staggering success, but the euphoria over its acclaim by the fashion world had slowly waned. Sarah was exhausted, and she could hardly wait for the plane to touch down at Mascot Airport where Ben and the children would be waiting for her. She had missed them so much and she was beginning to think that Ben was right about success. There came a time when it could be achieved almost too easily, became almost taken for granted. Maybe she should give the game up now. But there was still Paris . . .

'You're so lucky to have Ben to come home to.'

Sarah glanced her surprise at the young woman sitting beside her. She had thought that Penny would still be riding high. Her designs had won every possible accolade from the most discerning critics in the fashion world. Yet the words had been spoken on a despondent sigh.

'Yes, I am lucky,' Sarah agreed softly. She didn't have Penny Walker's creative brilliance, but not even a talent like that could ever measure up to what Ben gave her. Her heart lifted at the thought of being with him. Soon now.

Penny sighed again. 'The feeling of conquering one of the great bastions, there's nothing like it, yet afterwards . . .' She rolled her head towards Sarah, her mouth curled into an ironic smile. 'I guess I'll put my head down and design more dresses, more collections. That's all I have in my life. But to come home to someone like Ben . . . You've got everything a woman could ever want, Sarah.'

The ache of inner loneliness whispered behind every word and Sarah didn't know how to appease it. She reached over and squeezed Penny's hand. 'You'll find someone who loves you one day. Perhaps in Paris, some fine, dashing Frenchman who'll adore everything about you. He'll burst into your life and suddenly you'll feel you hadn't really lived before you met him.' She smiled in remembrance of her first meeting with Ben. 'I was twenty-eight when Ben swept me off my feet. Literally. You're only twenty-seven now, Penny. You'll meet someone. Some day.'

Penny's smile changed to one of hopeful whimsy. 'Well, I'll look forward to Paris.'

Sarah sank back into her own thoughts. She could no longer imagine a life without Ben. It would soon be their fifth wedding anniversary. She wondered how they would celebrate it this year. Ben always came up with some marvellous idea.

She would do the organisation for Penny's Paris

collection, Sarah decided, but it would definitely be the last. Her swan-song. In a funny kind of way she felt she owed it to Penny. Her mind slipped back to the conference at the store where it had all begun: Julian's call that had messed up Sarah's bid to tie up a contract with Penny. If she hadn't been so incensed by it, hadn't been so keen to get Penny's designs on sale . . . No. Ben and she would still have got together. Somehow. As Ben said, they had been made for each other. Still, the issue over Penny's contract had accelerated everything.

Amusement bubbled through her mind as she thought of Julian, married to Frances Chatfield. Ben had chuckled all day when they had heard about it. 'They're well matched so they'll probably be happy,' he had declared.

Sarah actually hoped they were, although she could not imagine any couple being happier than she and Ben. Sometimes it worried her a little that Ben didn't work at a regular job, but he was such an ideal father and he seemed so content doing whatever he was doing . . . and he had come up with the whirly-truck that flew, which was still selling well in the toy shops. But that was two years ago when Christopher had been eighteen months old and enchanted with all things mechanical.

Since then . . . not that it mattered. Even if Ben never came up with another selling idea, they had enough investments and income from the boutiques to keep them secure for the rest of their lives. Sarah smiled as she thought of Ashley Thompson and how she had taken to boutique management like a duck to water. Ashley was just like one of the family, sharing the apartment with Angela and becoming as involved as Sarah in the fashion business.

And Ben had set it all up. Sarah was quite sure that Ben would find a way to do anything. There was really nothing for her to worry about. And as long as he was happy at home with her and their family . . . that was the only important thing.

The jet engines went into reverse and the plane touched down. Sarah heaved a sigh of relief. Home at last. Excitement coursed through her as she joined the stream of passengers making their exit from the plane, and as soon as she set foot inside the terminal she was greeted by a triumphant shout from Christopher.

'Mummy! Mummy!'

The short, three-year-old legs pelted towards her and she swooped on him, catching him up in her arms and hugging him tight, as her gaze automatically searched for Ben. He was standing back, out of the way of the emerging crowd, a huge grin of welcome on his face and Sally perched on his shoulders, waving a chubby little hand at her.

A great surge of love wound around Sarah's heart. Her husband. Her family. 'I saw you first,

Mummy,' Christopher crowed in her ear as she carried him back to Ben. 'Kiss, Mummy,' Sally demanded, and was instantly hoisted from Ben's shoulders and held out to Sarah. Christopher slid down to give place to his little sister and Sarah cuddled her darling daughter and gave her lots of kisses.

'I think it's my turn,' Ben said, his eyes caressing Sarah with a desire that had not diminished at all over the years. She gave Sally into Christopher's charge and sank into Ben's strong embrace, savouring the wonderful sense of belonging he always gave her. 'Welcome home, darling,' he murmured, and his kiss was a sweet reminder of what they would share when the time was right.

They heard Penny talking to their children and quickly turned to gather her into their circle. Ben gave her a mock-salute, 'Hail to the conqueror!' and Penny laughed. 'Knew you were a winner, Penny,' Ben declared. 'Sarah's never wrong. That was a great triumph in London. We're all terribly proud of you.'

And Penny glowed under his congratulations as they all went to collect the luggage. Sarah slipped her arm around Ben's, hugging it possessively, loving him fiercely for being so nice, so kind, so giving. They saw Penny off in a taxi and then finally they were alone together in their own family car.

'We've got a big surprise for you at home, Mummy,' Christopher said excitedly.

'Big s'prise,' echoed Sally with happy emphasis.

Sarah raised her eyebrows at Ben.

'Big surprise,' he said smugly.

It was plain that she was not to be told. Even Christopher and Sally stood firm against her questions, and Ben's grin grew wider and wider. 'We'll show you as soon as we get home,' he promised, and with that she had to be content.

Honey and Tramp barked a feverish welcome from the backyard as they turned into the driveway. However, Sarah was not allowed to go and greet the dogs. The children were in such a fever of excitement by the time they had all alighted from the car that they literally dragged Sarah into the house.

'The family-room, Mummy,' Christopher directed.

'They're all there,' Sally crowed.

Ben threw the door of the family-room open with a flourish and there, sitting on the chairs and cupboards and shelves, was the most extraordinary collection of soft-toy creatures: fantasy animals that had to be the product of brilliant imagination, madly exaggerated, made in brilliant colour combinations, and the expressions on their faces so amusing and endearing that Sarah immediately fell in love with all of them.

'The Trendsetters,' Ben proudly announced.

'We helped Daddy make them up,' Christopher said just as proudly.

'And get the colours,' Sally said importantly.

Sarah gestured her amazement at their cleverness. 'They're the most marvellous creations I've ever seen.'

'We got the girls in Penny's factory to make them up for us while you were away,' Ben informed her with a delighted smile at her reaction. 'They loved them so much they've already put in orders. I think we're on to another big winner, Sarah.'

'Oh, yes!' Sarah agreed very positively. 'No doubt about it!'

Ben sighed. 'Unfortunately, it'll bring us another tax problem, Sarah. So I guess we'd better consider some more income splitting.'

Sarah's delight turned to a threatening glower. 'Now just a minute, Ben Haviland!'

His eyebrows shot up at her tone. 'Well, it's only sensible ...'

'If you're thinking of becoming a Mormon or a Muslim ...'

'Whatever for?'

'I've seen your solution to tax problems before, and I won't have you setting up a harem, or marrying another woman just to divide ...'

He burst out laughing and pulled her into a very

possessive hug. 'As if I would when I've got you, you crazy woman! I was thinking of a trust fund with the children as beneficiaries.'

'Oh!'

'But it's nice to know you don't want to share me,' Ben teased.

The jealous fierceness in her eyes melted into deep wells of love. 'Only with the children.'

And love shone back at her. 'Which reminds me,' Ben murmured huskily. 'I think it's time we got started on our third. If you want to?' It was a gentle question.

'I want to,' she sighed happily.

And much, much later, when Christopher and Sally were safely tucked into bed for the night, Ben rolled her into his arms and held her close. 'It's so good to have you home. Do you know why I love you so much?' he murmured.

Sarah reached up to touch his face, her fingers lightly tracing the tiny scar in his eyebrow, the dimples in his cheeks, the full sensual lips, caressing, loving. It didn't matter why she loved him. She just did. 'No,' she whispered.

'Because there's nothing about you I'd want to change. I knew that from the moment we met. You're perfect,' he breathed happily.

And a long time later when he was cradling her head over his heart, he said, 'What do you want to call the baby?'

Sarah knew that that didn't matter either. 'It's your turn to pick the names,' she said on a sigh of contentment, and snuggled closer.

She smiled as Ben tried out one name after another, examining them for advantages and disadvantages. He was still musing over several possibilities when Sarah drifted into sleep to dream the most perfect, wonderful dreams.

A BATTLE OF PASSION AND DENIAL

Freed from her tedious existence in England, Catrina sets sail for Gibraltar and her long lost family. She finds herself caught up in the tensions within the home and the onset of war with Spain.

Catrina falls hopelessly in love with the captain with the silvery eyes – the one man forbidden to her.

Can the secret of their illicit love remain hidden in an unforgiving society?

A colourful and stirring romance from Christina Laffeaty.

Available October Price £2.95

W✪RLDWIDE

Available from Boots, Martins, John Menzies, W H Smith, Woolworths and other paperback stockists.

ROMANCE

Variety is the spice of romance

Each month, Mills & Boon publish new romances. New stories about people falling in love. A world of variety in romance — from the best writers in the romantic world. Choose from these titles in October.

A LATE LOVING Robyn Donald
THE POSITIVE APPROACH Emma Darcy
BLACK DIAMOND Joanna Mansell
SHADOW IN THE SUN Elizabeth Power
REBEL WITH A CAUSE Leigh Michaels
SECRET PASSION Carole Mortimer
QUICKSANDS Elizabeth Oldfield
UNFRIENDLY ALLIANCE Jessica Steele
LOST LAGOON Anne Weale
A MOMENT OF ANGER Patricia Wilson
*GIFT BEYOND PRICE Annabel Murray
*DAUGHTER OF THE STARS Quinn Wilder
*BITTERSWEET PASSION Lynne Graham
*ROAD TO LOVE Katherine Arthur

On sale where you buy paperbacks. If you require further information or have any difficulty obtaining them, write to: Mills & Boon Reader Service, PO Box 236, Thornton Road, Croydon, Surrey CR9 3RU, England.

*These four titles are available from Mills & Boon Reader Service.

Mills & Boon
the rose of romance

ACCEPT 4
MILLS & BOON
ROMANCES
ABSOLUTELY FREE

...after all, what better way to continue your enjoyment of the finest stories from the world's foremost romantic authors? This is a very special introductory offer designed for regular readers. Once you've read your four **free** books you can take out a subscription (although there's no obligation at all). Subscribers enjoy many special benefits and all these are described overleaf. ► ► ►